UMBULALA

THROUGH THE EYES OF A LEOPARD

SO SINGS THE BAMBOOS OF AFRICA

LÉNA GODSALL BOTTRIELL

AUTHOR of
UMBULALA: The Jungle Book from the Heart of Africa

Artwork: Paul Bottriell
Photoprints: Paul Bottriell & Léna Godsall Bottriell

Rex Natura *Limited*

First Published in 2005 by
REX NATURA Limited
PO Box 141, Aylesbury, HP22 6YT, UK

of
THE REX FOUNDATION (UK)
- Wildlife Trust -
dedicated to the research and preservation of
cheetah and leopard, their habitats
and prey-bases

www.king-cheetah.freeservers.com
www.umbulala.com

A CIP catalogue record for this book is available from the British Library.
ISBN: 0 9521871 1 6

Printed by Compass Press Limited, London England

Also by Léna Godsall Bottriell

King Cheetah: **The Story of The Quest**
Published by E. J. Brill Leiden

Umbulala: **The Jungle Book From The Heart of Africa**
Published by Rex Natura Limited

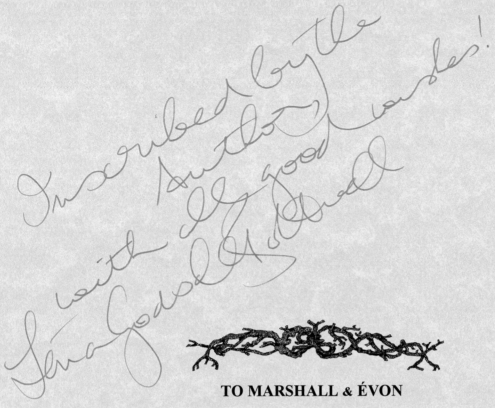

TO MARSHALL & ÉVON

*who made this onward
journey of Umbulala possible,*

PAUL
*whose continued
inspiration it is......*

*and, in thoughtful footnote,
the black cat
who walks with us still*

INTRODUCTION

Umbulala is a romance of wildest Africa at its purest. It documents the continuing saga of Umbulala, leopard supreme, and is no fairytale. Rather it is an adventure fantasy of the truest kind, wilderness in the raw - a plain tale out of Africa of the day-to-day existence of a magnificent big cat sculptured in the classic mould; one of that quintessential breed born to hunt, and as such among the most formidable of predators.

Leopards have inhabited very nearly the entire expanse of Africa and Asia, through every terrain and climactic zone, from near-desert to snowcapped mountain peak. While still eagerly sought after for their hide - and not least threatened by habitat loss, reduction in prey base animals, to 'indirect' human excesses, unspoken of and unaddressed - they are the most adaptable of cats, and as such a resilient species. Big game hunters, poachers and field zoologists alike consider leopard the most dangerous of animals: pound for pound, the jungle's most consistently successful hunter-killer; while among native peoples it is the most feared of the cats for its courage and tenacity, its cool, calculating patience.

The leopard is also one of the most beautiful of the wild's animals, capable of quite matchless tenderness as a mother, and in this alone surpasses all other cats with which it co-exists. Nature's paradox. Here lies one of those great contradictions of nature, often noted in brightly hued birds with voices of tuneless rasp; or the deceptive loveliness of prettily coloured or scented plants which disguise a poisonous intent. Many is the beast whose beauty belies its nature. No better does this apply than to the big cats of jungle and savanna; no better than to leopard. Yet as physically perfect, aesthetically pleasing creatures that they are, they can never be amiable pussycats chastened to be at humankind's beck and call. The individuality of each within the whole is inviolate. Nature's design for them is not to win approval, only respect. Umbulala is a panther - a term popularly applied to black leopards in Africa - born of the loins of the spotted leopard, Ingwe. This is not a story where the ferocity of the cat has been glossed over in a misplaced, anthropomorphic way; nor the dangers that lurk in what, in the minds of the uninitiated, is paradise. The bush, the jungle, is the most neutral of places, filled with beauty, abounding in sustenance for those with the care and wit to find it. It is also unforgiving, where all must walk a narrow path as with just one, careless step, injury or death awaits; perilous pitfalls to which predators are as susceptible as the animals upon which they prey.

Tripping in and out this on-going tale of Umbulala's adventurous wanderings, which ultimately take him to the lush volcanic realm of the equatorial regions - last bastion and homeland of the true Mountain gorilla - and the ice-capped *Lunae Montes* beyond, is the panther's recollections of cubhood and adolescence; reminiscences that miss neither the humour nor seemingly insignificant things of the jungle.....nor its many lessons. Umbulala is a leopard of such proportions as to compare favourably in size with an 18 month old lioness, gifted by nature with a sharp mind and instinct, aided by incomparable senses that are the hallmark of leopard: carnivore consummate, perfect distillation of the predator supreme. In essence a cat like no other - the stuff of legend.

CONTENTS

Deepest gratitude is extended to:

Praveen Moman for his generous hospitality and that of his management in Uganda – from Yusuf Mubiru at Volcanoes Kampala, to John Mugume and staff at Travellers Rest and Mount Gahinga for their cheerful attendance to all our needs, notably Moses for his calm presence, Medadi for his delicious cuisine, Richard and his zeal for nature – and, not least, their gracious colleague Andrew, Chairman of the Mountain Club of Uganda whose untimely, tragic death touched us all; Fölscher Roets and Alliance Air; Management and staff Sheraton Kampala for their always welcoming and accommodating support; intrepid Eagle Uganda who flew to parts others didn't; Ugandan High Commissioner to London, His Excellency Professor George Kirya for all his help; Uganda Ministry of Tourism, and Uganda Commissioner for Tourism, Wildlife, Antiquities Ms. Blandina Nshakira; Dr. Robbie Robinson Uganda Wildlife Authority, valued acquaintance from King Cheetah ventures in southern Africa, and colleague Lilly Ajarova; Ignatius Nakishero of UTB for his ready gestures of assistance; Byamukama Bonifence of Kitandara Travel for the photo; Debby Cox in Entebbe; the late Harry, and Senior Curator Peter Wait Chester Zoo; and lastly John Nagenda, advisor to the President, for his invaluable personal support.

THE JUNGLE IS NEUTRAL

Beware the cat that walks the night

As if shyly fanning the air through their leaves, the crowns of the yellow thorn Fever trees, arrayed in handsome splendour along the riverbank, swayed in the breeze. A bountiful wet season of rain and growth was easing the inexorable onset of another long, cloying *dry*. Yet little that was noticeable to the eye had altered: every tree was still a resplendent posy of lime coloured leaves, the dappled shadows of each, dancing and sashaying along the bank, mimicking in inky detail the branched foliage of these lovely yellow-barked acacias.

While still relatively deep after the deluge of the wet, the river adjacent to the trees had begun to narrow noticeably, shrinking back from the banks with every sunrise that dusted the dawn. And as the flow would become more restricted to the middle of the riverbed with the steady, onward march of the *dry* - as much victim of the seasonal change as first the flora, then the fauna would be - gradually more of the sandbanks either side would become exposed; to the point of actually linking up in parts by way of the reed clumps that dotted the watercourse like miniature, tropic isles.

Thus it was, at a river prospect so distinctly marked out, Umbulala's territory halted. He hadn't the remotest need, or desire, to expand it beyond the Fever trees. Besides being sufficiently extensive for a male leopard of his calibre, the opposing bank backed on to a strip of indifferent scrub and spindly trees which

in turn fell away to a vast vista of open grassland. It appealed little to the panther, rolling monotonously on as far as the eye could see. By contrast, his preferred territorial range favoured a welcome abundance of cover, in a generous weave of trees and bush that started life at the river. Meandering back from the Fever trees over a wide aspect of bushland and jungle, it was a terrain dotted with kopjes, outcrops and clearings, waterholes and other natural interruptions of varying size, shape, and significance. To add to this attractive mix, only a dawn to dusk amble from the river fringes the land climbed; as it did the vegetation thinned to taller more open forest, before melding to heavier cover that rolled on in a veritable jumble of flora up to the lofty hills that formed a natural boundary round it. A crescent of interconnected buttes, plateaux and downs, it girdled the panther's range by virtue of being linked by a wide escarpment which dropped back to the lower tracts that then ran on, and away, to the river, its final frontier. Over all this Umbulala claimed dominion.

Shunning the clan system so favoured by lion, leopards are solitary by nature, with little liking for other cats - a penchant that naturally stops short of leopards of the opposite gender. Needless to say, when desirous of being so acquainted, notably for the purpose of mating, a tenacious leopard will follow a contact all the way; only to be off reasonably swiftly if random observance is any guide. Even so, that the parting must be immediate or permanent is by no means mandatory. Umbulala, for one, rendezvoused often with Tola his first mate, now with two small cubs down by the low escarpment; interimly hunting with her, sometimes allowing the cubs to share the kill; even, as the Scimitar-billed hoopoe let it be known, to play with his tail, all of course under the solicitous eye of Tola. General observation may well deem such behaviour the exception. However, given the subject is leopard, it is only right, and fair, to add one crucial qualification: it is behaviour that is rarely *observed*, and with observation the operative factor, herein lies the conundrum - and it's a conundrum that sits perfectly with the leopard's renown for avoiding detection, and as such impossible to claim with certainty just how uncommon among leopards.

What *is* certain is that most male leopards are too unpredictable on the matter of cubs; a trait all to do with an age-old territorial imperative that affects relationships between adult males and unrelated cubs among all the big cats. Add quick-tempered, nearly always hungry - the latter not confined to males - and it's a powerful mix untempered by subtleties such as 'maternal bond'. Only in the wet season just gone did Umbulala have two encounters, in the sanctity of his own territory too, that couldn't have impressed on him more just how important it is to be always wary of any fellow leopard - male or female.

The Crowned crane was the first to raise the alarm. The elegant bird had caught sight of the panther nipping through the shadows. In an instant reflex action a colony of Weavers had noisily taken off - only to quickly return once they'd discovered what the alarm was about. Umbulala felt vaguely amused, not to mention a touch irritated, by the noisy protestations of the little birds over being torn away from what to him, a predator way above the tittle-tattle of the tittering things of the jungle, was a constant barrage of prattle! *But it's the small things that grow into greater things to come*, retaliatory thoughts superciliously teased, recalling one of his mother Ingwe's more cogent philosophies. Like the humble stream that becomes a great river, the meagre seed a mighty baobab.......and Umbulala sighed, steeling himself to concentrate his senses to take it *all* in, and not merely disregard something because of a seeming lack of importance. Indeed, as he'd been taught.

And it was as well the panther did; otherwise his gaze mightn't have lingered on a sight he may have dismissed as deserving of minor attention. The grass ahead had been bent over and flattened a little; while a twig on a thorn bush had been broken and was hanging down. He approached, and on sniffing around was hit by a powerful scent. But something about it at once unnerved him, the fur on the back of his neck bristling instantly in reaction. The scent niggled again at nostrils ultra-sensitive to the slightest subtlety, the tiniest tinge of anything out of sync - in short, not quite right. It was that of a leopard, a female about to come into season. Yet, oddly, far from attracting him, it repulsed him......and the panther grunted fretfully under his breath:

"I should be excited; have....have I, *could* I have passed my prime already!"

Taking another long sniff, his whole being was now convinced something was very wrong. All of his senses enguard, the panther slinked forward a distance. Keeping to the cover of heavy scrub he slipped like honey over hot rock, up on to a large whaleback of stone - a flattish granite intrusion rearing from the ground - watched over by a towering Pod Mahogany. Enveloped in the heavy shade of the tree's handsome, spreading crown, it made a fine vantage point on which to shape his muddle of thought into some order.

It wasn't the flattened grass, nor the extent of it; not even the twig - or the level at which it had been broken - that nagged at him. It was just the smell, the very taint of it. It left him with nothing like the fluttery feelings he felt whenever he met up with Tola - *he'd been knocked off his paws at their first meeting!* No; with this scent something plainly malodorous and off-putting, almost repellent, confused and concerned him all in the same breath. He was pondering this contradiction when a sharp breeze suddenly whipped up out of nowhere. Stinging his face and whiskers with resolve, it whirled about the stony promontory sculptured smooth by the elements:

"Little brothh-hherrr....."

he thought he heard it sigh as it nipped about his ears, eyes and snout,

"Mother nature has instilled in you wisdom and patience, yet you are strangely restless - and not a little disturbed!"

The panther sniped back, more irritated with his own inability to get a grip of his confusion, than any seemingly senseless intervention of the wind:

"There's something wrong - but what.....!?"

Dropping its intensity a gentler breeze at once began to blow about the big cat:

"Indeed there is, and from it you will certainly learn something new, and with only a minimum of danger; if, that is, you're wise."

Growing increasingly piqued Umbulala growled softly under his breath. Already not best pleased, he was even less in the mood for riddles. Casting himself off the granite slab, he hissed his displeasure at the wind and flounced off. But blessed as cats are with an enviable quality of rapid self-control, he soon calmed. Safe again in a cool, hunter's frame of mind, he'd barely gone a few paces when a lofty eruption in the shape of a gigantic spherical boulder balanced on a rock sill - of such proportions it was impossible to pass without paying deference to its grandeur - loomed ahead. Weathered over time to a great globular chunk of stone, he duly cut his pace, his intention to skirt it, then continue on toward a rambling grove beyond of Waterberry trees, where they graced a stretch of riverine territory he hadn't visited for some moons.

But he was ahead of himself. As he drew alongside the boulder, his eye was straightaway drawn to a point in the treeline just emerging into sight from behind the masking effect of the rock. Something about it was luring his gaze to linger longer, and wouldn't let go. Halting instantly in his tracks as if stung by a hornet, the big cat stared hard; a heartbeat later he'd slipped into the burrowing shade of the boulder's underside where, crouched comfortably, the consummate binocular vision of the felid began to scrutinize and dissect the treeline. It was but a tiny movement in the lower storey of the tree canopy which initially caught his attention; that the boulder should make an opportune stopping-place in the interim to observe from awhile, was just too tempting an enticement to pass up.

Umbulala narrowed his gaze, his pupils dilating to specks as he focused in on the anonymous presence in the tree cover that had captured his interest so compellingly. When another small movement shook the foliage it gave the panther his first clear view. He recognised it immediately. It was the tip of a tail. Sharp eyes rifled through the mottled shadows, and with piercing precision began to decipher a spotted form; a spotted form stretched along a branch in a pose all too familiar. Leopard! When a momentary hush later he judged the cat to be female by the cut and size of her head, he knew for certain. Apart from the hard evidence, his instinct was also informing him in that confirmatory way normal rationale can't explain; a way that had never let him down when it mattered. The cat in the tree was the mysterious female leopard, the haunting traces of whom had been so exercising his attention.

She looked to be no more than a third his size. Despite this Umbulala didn't move a muscle - approaching every leopard with caution his guiding mantra.

As searching eyes probed and inspected, he was all too soon taken aback by something he least expected. Not a terrible wound or deformity, but her hide - one of the glories, be they black or spotted, of leopard. Here in this instance a spotted leopard. But not the richly rosetted, honied gold of the leopard in good health; instead, a moth-eaten greyish brown with just a sprinkling of the trademark rosettes - around her paws, the crown of her head and lower part of her tail. That was all. Umbulala was about to get a closer look. Lifting herself up off the branch, she stretched; then sliding down the smooth trunk into an open strip of ground between the stand of trees and the boulder, she began to stroll unhurriedly away in the direction of the river, hidden from view beyond the Waterberry trees.

Her gait didn't give away a hint of illness. Without yet attempting to follow, Umbulala watched her slowly meld into cover. He was absolutely enthralled. But not by any beauty, or power of physique. Her fur was not fur at all! It was as if the leopardess's hide had decayed into scabby, bare skin, heavily pocked and raw, as though she'd been constantly scratching herself to rid her body of some virulent vermin. Such a virtually naked cat among the living was something Umbulala had never before encountered; nor had he ever heard of the like it. This leopard was a wretched sight to behold, and as the panther's mind raced, he involuntarily let slip a questioning grunt into the air as to what might ail her; even to wondering if it had something to do with hairless apes. They never seemed far from what was unnatural or unspeakable, or so it seemed to Umbulala.

Just then a sudden wind gust blasted Umbulala's way, breezing into his face and eyes and whistling eerily about his ears;

"Not hairless apes - but the curse of *mange.....*"
it droned soberly back,

"that creeps unseen and unsuspected from animal to animal to ensnare the unwary in its grasp. Hence your instinct to stay well clear. Heed that inner wisdom Umbulala, and *learnnnnn*!"

The leopardess was ambling along the riverbank when the panther caught up with her. He chose to keep a generous distance between them; a choice doubtless emboldened by the knowledge this was an affliction that spread. She was a pathetic sight: undernourished and debilitated, he could now see from close up; a state that would be affecting her judgement, and probably explain her aberrant behaviour. After all - no grown leopard of sound mind will wander so nonchalantly in the open as this leopard was now doing, let alone along a riverbank without remotely attending to the general surroundings, to what skulked about ahead or to the rear; more especially, what lurked around the immediate river margins where a multitude of perils can lie in wait. It was as if this leopard was eking out her life in a daze. It was an uncommonly pitiful sight to witness; and it was one that was impacting on more than just the panther, as even a small herd of usually ever-vigilant wildebeest nearby hadn't bothered to snort an alarm! There could be no better confirmation of his assessment.

Already exposed to whoever might be watching with malicious intent, she went on to compromise herself further by flopping down in carefree abandon at the river's edge In as vulnerable position as she could put herself - a situation not relieved by even the vaguest allusion to any cover in a screen of reeds or a clutch of grass - she next began to scratch away unrestrainedly like the simplest-minded pup. When she then lent forward to lap greedily at the water, every part of Umbulala screamed in silent rebellion at a leopard who, thirst now completely the captor of her senses, could so plainly forsake all vestige of survival instinct, her last refuge. A breeze tripped gently over the sun-kissed water, tracing small ripples along its surface, playing about the spotted leopard. To the untutored eye it was the

classic wilderness idyll of romantic imagination, a halcyon, scenic vignette - so tranquil and unthreatening birds could be excused a rest from singing. To the seasoned observer it presented an altogether different picture.

Not restful, but ominous was the silence that had fallen over the river. Umbulala checked his environs so keenly did he sense Brother error, and shadowy companion death capering closely behind. At the moment the panther's eyes fell back on the ailing leopard still drinking in the shallows, the water in front of her erupted. Caught totally by surprise by a crocodile, she hadn't a chance. Scaly nemesis - the wild's most persistently efficient killer - it didn't have to even fully emerge: once powerful pincer jaws were agrip of the cat it just lifted its monstrous head, and using the weight of its body in conjunction with the current, slid backward into the river. Swinging away from the bank, the leopardess wedged firmly in its jagged mouth, the forbidding reptile glided effortlessly off - soulless yellow eyes glinting in the long, blunt head held above the water, just a bewhiskered snout and one twitching paw jutting out. Once well out in midstream the big saurian sank with its prey, only a tell-tale patch of bubbles to mark the passing of yet another victim.

Umbulala had watched spellbound throughout. It had all been so swift, neat almost, and with a barely perceptible snipe of surprise he reflected on what slim chance she'd had.

"She didn't need one…"

a sudden breeze seemed to whisper back, echoing his thoughts,

"for she was dying; illness had so dulled her senses and impaired her abilities she had lost touch with reality…..though it's true more leopards are taken by crocodiles than are ever killed by lions!"

Umbulala let out a shocked snarl of disbelief. It was one surprise too many and sent his imagination reeling, thought tumbling over thought, each more excessive than the last until one - *if leopards taken by crocodiles might even be as many as the hairless apes killed* - brought a stinging riposte on the wind:

"NNNooo....."it appeared to whine about him, stunning the cat to his senses, urging some perspective "for next in line is starvation...."

it blew with growing intensity

"followed by death from any number of illnesses worse than mange."

Umbulala snapped at the breeze:

"You're full of fun Wind, you know that? Have you any other enlightening
gems of information with which to smite my senses and terrorize me....?
The breeze whipped back through a spray of foliage just above the panther's
head:

"You can't waste priceless moments in the jungle having fun..."
it appeared to chide as it whirled sharply in and out the leaves,

"for there are many watchful eyes. Your mother Ingwe instilled in you much
that you need to know about hygiene, just so you don't fall foul of disease.
The jungle is neutral; be judicious, stay in good grace with your senses and
you will live to be old and much feared; be arrogant, and death will dance off
with you. Remember little brother…"
the breeze dropped, seeming to coax,

"you're never too wise to learn."

There was little one could add to that. Umbulala slipped away, wiser to be
sure, and certainly with an enhanced respect for crocodiles. Retracing his tracks
back past the boulder, then on to his wayside granite nook of earlier, he nimbly
scurried up the Mahogany, then out under its shiny-leaved crown onto a
generous branch. Here the big cat stretched out. As he began to luxuriate in a
soothing half-sleep much needed after such a sobering event, all four legs freely
dangling, chin rested on a higher bough, more calming thoughts of cubhood,
encouraged perhaps by the restorative touch of nature, began to work and weave
their way in and around his mind, tripping and tumbling about like cubs at play.

Crocodile

WISDOM DOWN THE SEASONS

The thorns whistle a tune for the reeds to dance to

ncircling the jungle was a broad field of terrain where the cover of trees and plant life thinned dramatically. It had all once been unbroached, untrod soil for Umbulala until, one sunrise, he and his sister Sibindi ventured there as fumbling adolescents on their very first foray into open bush country, and all under the expert tutelage of their mother Ingwe.

Some habitués of savanna and grassland are rarely seen in the deeper jungle spaces favoured by leopards. For many animals such country allows for far freer passage of movement than a more rank weave of flora. Stands of trees tall and well-spaced, loose scrub scattered between airy clearings, or open grassy stretches are all more conducive to easy strolling, and as such more open bush holds a greater attraction for most grazing ungulates and browsers able to roam with greater ease in family groups, or small herds. A sunrise or so on again the outlook of the land altered further as it gave on to wide swathes of grassland that swept all the way to the horizon, and beyond.

The trials and errors of life veritably feed the learning process - and there were trials and errors aplenty in this bush country. As the panther gazed dreamily back down the seasons, it certainly seemed so as cubs. Yet although he and Sibindi weren't exactly infants at this juncture Ingwe still deemed it prudent to be in attendance, just in case one or other got out of their depth. That they did was often out of a natural enthusiasm to impress. He recalled how, as a whole, scrubby or thorny tracts didn't throw up too many difficulties or problems for them; nothing they couldn't get round with some thought and care - and the notion things hadn't altered much in adulthood sighed through his mind! The uninterrupted golden spread of grasslands - now that by contrast, for Umbulala at any rate, was in a league of its own. Ingwe and Sibindi got by well enough in their spotted coats. For Umbulala in his gleaming coat of jet it was an altogether different proposition. Ingwe, of course, was only too aware how he was at an obvious disadvantage in such habitat. Any relief in its gilded expanse by way of some oases of camouflage in rocky outcrops - with any number of shady nooks and crannies - or leafy groves of trees was few and far between. However, it was Ingwe's foremost desire to instil in her young, above all else, a *know thyself* ethos; only by cubs confronting their weaknesses, as much as their abilities, can they hope to overcome obstacles inevitably cast their way in the seasons that stretch ahead.

Journeying to these unfamiliar bush tracts followed a deliberate pattern of moving in the small hours so to arrive with the rising sun as it burst gold and pink across the sky. But it wasn't all poesy and aesthetics that prompted Ingwe's timing. Rather a more plainly down-to-earth reason: in the moon splashed blue-blackness prior to dawn the going is cooler, and the cover infinitely better. Yet what held profoundest sway in Umbulala's memory was how Ingwe endeavoured to make the learning fun, humour as the great leveller, and as such a matchless aide-mémoire vastly under utilized as a rule. For her it was simply a matter of course - just another reason why her influence would never dim with the seasons. Thus while twilight through to dawn was for getting about, daylight was for lying up in accommodating trees and observing life. Only from such vantage points, with all of them safely ensconced out of harm's way and in relatively relaxed mode, could Ingwe draw attention to the many vagaries and absurdities of jungle life; the qualities and shortcomings of each animal that happened by, the highs and lows of every situation played out below them. As happened at his first meeting with giraffe.......and the big cat cringed at the recollection; worse, the encounter with Black rhino when his reckless foolishness very nearly cost him his life.

   The leopard family had strayed into a vast spread of scrub, a fair portion of it rolling banks of thorn thicket, and some so closely bunched together in places it was just a mass of grey to the eye. Halfway round one dense brake Umbulala stumbled on a large cavity, like a bolt-hole opening into a cavernous run that appeared to invitingly wind all the way into the thicket. Feline curiosity getting the better of any moue or murmurs from wiser quarters who might be urging caution, the young Umbulala gaily blundered in. He began at once to nose his way along; but all too precipitately for his own good. The tunnel-like shape of the thorn utterly intrigued him, luring him further and further. More and more unable to exercise restraint, the deeper it burrowed into the thicket, the more fascinated did he become - a fascination that rapidly turned to terrible unease the moment the ground under him suddenly began to tremble.

   All at once he felt horribly alone; no more so than when a snatched glance behind confirmed the worst. Ingwe and Sibindi were nowhere in sight!

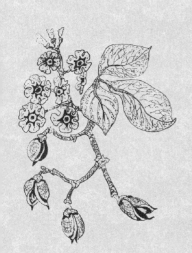

Symptomatic of the young male who's one among females - *doting* females as he might perceive them - Umbulala had just taken it for granted they'd followed. He would never do so again; and even now, a grown cat, he could still feel welling up from his stomach - to squeeze his gullet and throat in some strangled screech for help - that bitter taste of emptiness in the dread feeling of being alone in a hostile world, far removed from all one holds safe. A feeling undimmed down the seasons, back then it was being increasingly fed by a stertorous wheezing and snorting getting closer by the heartbeat; that it should be accompanied by the scraping sound of a heavy entity brushing against the thorn as it rushed in his direction left Umbulala in little doubt.

There are times in life when one simply doesn't need it explained that something nasty and unstoppable is heading one's way! In his meagre experience all the young panther could think of was elephant - and he didn't relish encountering any pachyderm in these tight quarters. A quick glance up the tunnel endorsed his wildest notions. Not elephant - but monstrous pachyderm in the guise of two blurred shapes, looking as big as hippos, thundering down on him. Protruding from above their snouts were a set of horns, one in front of the other, the nearmost growing bigger with every thump of his heart. The intention was clear, and being most decidedly the obstacle in the way of the inexorable force, the young panther did what any sane creature would do - he hightailed it back down the tunnel and out the thicket, any self-confidence or soupçon of swank all swept away!

With an excellent view out from a tall Acacia looking across the thicket, Ingwe waited for her errant cub. Watchful as ever, she lounged on a branch high up off the ground under the feathery-leaved spread of its crown. Sibindi was sat-stood alongside, the eager expression of uncontrolled curiosity that lit her features - as she hungrily tracked every disconnected bound of the wild-eyed cat lurching toward them - proclaiming all her cubbish thoughts in one: *what exciting new discovery has my big brother made.......!*

"Ahhh....he does move so well,"

Ingwe purred, half to herself, half to Sibindi

"and with such agility, when the need arises."

Without any direct knowledge of where his family were, sheer instinct for survival was taking Umbulala straight toward the sanctuary of the Acacia, vaulting up it in one spurt of adrenalin, and desperation.

"Mind the thorns!"

his mother crooned as he swept up the trunk and a limb or two in a single forward thrust of motion. Umbulala was simply impervious to claw-sharp thorns long as a cat's whisker, having left all feeling behind with his dignity in the thicket. In his reckoning mere spikes didn't much compete with a rhino horn beaming in on his rectum. Ingwe gazed at her cub - with heaving flanks, and bulging eyes that were giving every indication they might pop from their sockets:

"Umbulala...."

she nodded, her soft, soughing tone caustically restrained, and as such unforgettable,

"you *surely* picked up the powerful scent yet still strolled on, even when Wind warned you - ignoring that meant you chose to be a fool - after which you then very quickly made the acquaintance of the owners of the scent."

All these moons on he could still feel the barbs - and not just of the thorns, but of the stinging chastening that continued, every nuance of which he recalled in vivid detail:

"No wise cat crosses paths with rhino - and especially not in a rhino tunnel running directly into a thorn thicket. Elephants might on occasion make a stand against them....."

Inqwe impressed on him,

"but leopards do *not!*"

The cubs went on to discover how there were two types of rhino in their demesne; the smallest of the two being the 'black' - the more irascible ones Umbulala had just met so unceremoniously - who, as browsers, hold their proportionately short head higher than their bigger relations.

"And that prehensile lip...."

Ingwe declaimed on a more playful, albeit teasing note,

"did you not see it, Umbulala? The pointed upper lip, which allows them to browse so effortlessly on leaves, twigs, buds; even on spiky or thorny trees or shorter, bushier versions of this one. And did you, perchance, notice the bouncing trot and agility for ones so stout and sturdy? Impressive, don't you agree Umbulala!"

she purred rhetorically, and to the young Umbulala's relief, a little less tersely.

Ingwe coached the cubs long and hard. They learned how Black rhinos trot as if running on their toes, not dissimilar in motion to warthog; how heavy as they are they will turn in their own length, and are notoriously ill-tempered, attacking anything without provocation. *Anything* was Ingwe's unequivocal warning, before following with what, to the cubs, was almost joyful news in that the other type of rhino they would in time encounter,

similar in colour but more massive, was slower and quite inoffensive by comparison. Indeed so placid at times that White rhinos - only beaten in size and strength by hippos and elephants - can often appear quite helpless and bewildered, though one is best advised not to test them too stringently on this! Be that as it may, Umbulala far preferred the sound of this rhino. Holding its head lower, with a distinct hump at its shoulders and a broader, square muzzle ideal for a grazer, the difference is readily recognisable. The rest was forged forever into memory. After learning how either rhino can nearly always be identified by the snorting sound it makes, Ingwe had turned a burning gaze back on the young panther:

"You surely noticed the exhaling surge of air before the snort - when you hear that, it means take cover."

It was a final reproach calculated never to be forgotten, and Umbulala hadn't, hissing under his breath as much. Such a blow was it to his self-esteem he'd gone on to wonder if Brother wind would spread tales of his idiocy through the jungle, before thinking he heard, almost in the same breath, a breeze whistling back through the thorns about how such lessons, not easily learned, are common to all, and thus nothing to warrant the attention gossip accords. Umbulala's pangs of dejection aside, Ingwe was pleased. No one had been hurt - only ego, a temporary pain necessary to the learning process; while much of what was being experienced on these adventures further afield was proving most worthwhile. Moreover, with each that passed Ingwe - for now, crucial wellspring of the cubs' existence - grew increasingly assured they would use the wisdom they gleaned to stride with confidence, tempered by prudence, into a future in which she wouldn't be constantly around to guide. It was an assurance the mother leopard no less deserved for a matchless devotion that would repay itself many fold. And so it would one day prove without Ingwe so much suspecting, let alone expecting it.

When the source of Umbulala's embarrassment had long lumbered off, Ingwe abruptly sat up - still, silent, and with the cool look of resolve the cubs knew so well. A distant movement in the opposite direction to where the rhino had decamped had caught her eye, and she was quietly watching, and analysing it. After some moments of intent observation the big leopardess dropped from the tree onto the ground in one swoop. Turning to trot on, she beckoned her young in one and the same motion to follow. Mindful of the prickly route out of the tree they weren't yet of the experience, or confidence of their mother to so slickly negotiate, Sibindi and Umbulala tentatively picked their way down toward terra firma. But once free of the thorns there was no holding them, and duly hastened after her. In the way of adolescents the going was interrupted by the usual antics: a playful cuff here, a tackle there, in between much rolling about before the last, mad dash to catch up.

A leopard mother keeps a brisk pace. Fortunately for young leopards nature provides for this by endowing her with the inspired notion of holding her tail upright - and with it being white-tipped on the underside, Ingwe's tail bobbing along like a guiding star above the scrub and long grass was a perfect point of reference for trailing youngsters. She came to a halt at an imposing granite outcrop. Rambling in and around the hilly pile of boulders and rocks balanced one on top of another, stunted bushes and knots of grass interlaced along the gaps and joints to give the impression of one great rock wreathed in a mesh of vegetation. Ingwe was already up the top of it peering out from behind a mask of greenery when the two young leopards joined her. They followed her gaze - and quickly lost interest, drawing a sharp rebuke from Ingwe, long-accustomed to the impatient and restless body movements of offspring:

"You're not looking with the eyes of hunters! Look deeper: sight, hearing...." she intoned encouragingly,

"and patience are all among the great assets of a leopard. Use them - there is something out there worthy of your attention."

A glossy coated impala ram lifted his head. Flashing pointed ears forward, there followed a sharp, high-pitched bark of alarm. At the instant it sounded the air around billowed into a sprawling swell of impalas leaping and spiralling skyward: a balletic high-flying retreat from peril in a swirling arabesque of jumps, jetés and sweeping bounds practised many times. Something was in full flight after them, a blurred, sleek streak slicing toward the herd at breathtaking speed. The cub's immediate sense was of an eagle, a Martial, or some other of that fine ilk of feathered hunters swiftly skimming just over the grass; and at the notion of a mighty bird of prey taking on an impala, his attention was at once gripped. A heartbeat later there was a hit. Only when the dust settled was the root cause of the mayhem revealed. It stood up.....and it wasn't an eagle but a lanky felid taller than any leopard. Holding an impala by the throat the slim spotted cat turned a smouldering gaze on the outcrop from where it was under such rapt scrutiny, its large eyes blazing amber in the sunlight. Umbulala coughed in a wonder of surprise and admiration:

"It was so fast, just a blur.....I took it to be an EAGLE flying flat-out over the grass!"

Ever the consummate teacher, worthily savouring the fruit of her earnest endeavours, Ingwe purred back with ready enthusiasm, a satisfied twinkle in her expression:

"Quite so. Here before us, little ones, is the fastest of *all* animals; one that is faster than even the fleetest of antelopes or gazelles, and in grassland such as this so difficult to focus on when sprinting at full pelt, their legs and paws defy recognition. Likening it to an eagle skirting the grass tops is most apt."

With Sibindi's sharp observation on how 'huge', or rather, higher off the ground than leopard it stood, Umbulala recalled with pleasure his mother's unfolding tale of Ingwelulu: the unique felid, closest in outward appearances to leopard out of all the big cats, yet so very different.

"Not so much huge…."

Ingwe mewled back,

"as elegantly statuesque. Nature's great running cats - svelte, upright and built for the chase - distinctive unto themselves."

And with that tantalizing opener Ingwe went on to beguile her two enthralled cubs with more on the amazing cheetah; how one drawback of being the fastest of all - if drawback it is - is that the cheetah's slender build and slight jawline leaves it at a disadvantage against heavier rivals, with sometimes even a single hyaena - the deadliest jaws in the game which can crush bone to powder - able to chase them off a kill when the occasion arises. For all that, Ingwe's reverence for the cats born to run was clear. Just as the sight of a Bateleur eagle or a swallow, tumbling or gliding through the air - that both appear to do for the sheer joy of flying - can so pleasure the eye, it was as if her respect for a predator that looked like it hunted for the sheer joy of the *chase* was unbounded, and that was that.

"Of course....."

she purred in afterthought,

"if there's two or more together they'll not necessarily back off. Indeed, I've seen two cheetah fend off a pair of hyaena; and one lone cheetah chase an adolescent leopard as big as you two, there being no doubt about its intention to kill - if the leopard hadn't fortuitously escaped up a tree."

He could never forget her final anecdote on the clinching difference between himself and Ingwelulu. Cheetah have blunt claws that, being only partially retractable, act somewhat as spikes, and are absolutely ideal for a high-speed sprinter to grip the ground. The reverse applies to leopards: sharper, more treacherous hooked claws can be fully withdrawn into protective sheathes and 'rested', so to keep them from getting blunt, or extended fully and used to such masterly effect with prey, or to hook and grip and hoist themselves up when climbing.

"There is one, potent reason why the cheetah avoids confrontation - like no other predator…"

ran Ingwe's thoughtful, closing assessment,

"its life depends on its gift to run, and any injury to a muscle, leg or paw can be fatal."

A cheetah is temporarily drained of breath after a long chase at the speeds it touches. Hence, with its slighter build and relatively smaller head and short jaws, any scrap directly after such an expulsion of energy would be, needless to say, foolhardy. And foolhardiness is not the cheetah's suit. Cheetahs still remain, regardless of factors such as increased competition for food, the most successful hunters of the savannas, bettering even lion; like leopard, perfectly balanced in the jungle's cycle of life.

"So be circumspect - short, sharp and accurate…"

Umbulala recalled Ingwe nodding deliberately at each of them in turn,

"rather than just blundering in. *Learn* from the running cat."

A cogent observation to be sure; and one that cut to the quick - for one cub at least. Umbulala had another lasting cubhood memory of cheetah which, as much for the set of circumstances as for the behaviour of the cats involved, would stay with him as long as he had breath. Watching on yet another occasion from a secluded hide, again high up on a rocky promontory, a cheetah off on its own from a sibling group of three strolled into their sightline. What occurred next was more a comment on life, than any recklessness. The cat suddenly sprang upwards in the air like a pronking gazelle, moved sharply forward a few paces shaking a leg, before stopping in its tracks to stare back quizzically at the ground behind it. It had been bitten by a snake.

"Mother nature may not have given snakes legs with which to run…"

Ingwe had coughed lightly under her breath,

"but she gave them a powerful, often deadly bite, especially those with frontal fangs such as mambas and cobras; or those we leopards encounter more frequently - the tree-loving boomslangs. These, notwithstanding their back-fixed fangs and being shyer than the others, still carry a lethal juice."

Many such snakes are hard to spot: the puff adder in open country, where it will lie sluggishly on the ground; the Gaboon viper in heavier jungle, craftily concealed in among the dense ground coverage of shed leaves and the like.

"Both are perfectly camouflaged for their environments...."
the big leopardess solemnly warned,

"and deadly as you'll now see!"

And they did. The affect on the cat, svelte and slight as cheetahs are, was all but instantaneous. After wandering a way, more and more distressed of manner, it started to quiver, then as quickly again shudder all over. Before long it was unable to stand, collapsing under some bushes; shortly after it succumbed to the type of venom, going by its behaviour, that hits the nervous system, causing irreparable muscle breakdown. Death doesn't take long. For this unfortunate cheetah it was all over in less than it takes a Fish eagle to catch a bream on the wing and land back on its favourite perch to feed. Snakes either have hollow teeth, or a groove down the outside. So when they close their mouths to bite they pump their venom directly into the victim. Umbulala was quickly disillusioned by Ingwe that snakes only specialized in cheetahs:

"While it's usually small lizards, rodents and birds - *any* animal can be bitten...."
she impressed on them with increasing gravity

"of which most will die! Some snakes look small, but can still kill a zebra!"

There was a particularly poignant end to it all. Calling in their plaintive *chirrup,* the two remaining cheetahs took between a sunrise and two sunsets to look for their dead brother. On eventually finding his body slumped lifelessly beneath the brush, they spent a long while scenting, nudging and pawing him. When at last accepting they couldn't rouse him, that he was indeed dead and gone, they straightened up. Sleek-backed and stately, each in turn lifted its head high in the regal way of their kind, glanced for a bit about the immediate area, before turning to peer over the wider scene and on into the far distance; a remedial ritual to as much, perhaps, gather their senses, as check their surrounds. In long, languorous strides they then strolled serenely away. The leopards never saw them again.

Although these disparate experiences intrigued, even excited Umbulala, he was far happier back in the thicker cover of forest and jungle. It better suited his coat colouring after all; Sibindi, by contrast, didn't mind either way - just 'happy-to-be-a-huntin', seemed her motto. *What a cat* the grown panther reflected wistfully, and as he did he was right back there with Sibindi on another one of Ingwe's bush forays - this occasion at the elephant-beds just as sunrise was licking awake the morning. A filmy mist hung low as the leopards stealthily edged their way round a patch of woodland. Ingwe was bringing up the rear, the cubs side by side in front. The unexpected apparition of a massive anthill suddenly loomed up out of the dewy gloom. With visibility poor, it was less a shock than fortuitous, because the abandoned mound turned out to be an eminently convenient vantage spot from which to look out over the surrounding area, its crown sighted well above ground level where the mist was heaviest.

Despite being well into the *dry*, the spiky-topped tambookie grass still stood tall as an impala. Stretching out around the ample crest of the ant-heap, the three cats settled in for some quiet observation. Soon the mood floated off into one of trance-like tranquillity, its soporific pull so mesmerizing, so hypnotic, Sibindi and Umbulala found themselves following Ingwe, without any conscious decision to do so, into dreamily licking their coats. Little wonder then, that when ghostly shapes began to tower up in the murky haze to mooch silently about the anthill, the cubs were more than ill-prepared - they were shocked fit to burst. Everywhere monstrous termite mounds looked to be on the move. In reality elephants, one by one, were rising from their night beds but paces from the ant-heap. To the vocal accompaniment of a stream of satisfied stomach rumbles, in duet with the slapping of great, leathery ears against hides, the gargantuan forms began to feed, rhythmically ripping out grassy clumps with their trunks, tapping each against a leg to shake off the grit, before popping them in their mouths.

"Elephants nap standing up during the day....."

Ingwe ventured to draw the cubs out of themselves, stunned rigid as they still were by what was erupting around them,

"and only very late at night will they lie down and sleep for a short spell; moreover, you *will* always know when they're around because even in sleep they flap their ears....."

she purred, not a little amused at the picture it conjured up,

"while their stomach rumbles are a means of communicating - of advising, of warning. Similarly the messages they reputedly send through the ground with the stamping of their feet; vibrations like waves on the great lake only elephants hear or detect, and which can apparently cross distances vast as our territory in the beat of a dragonfly's wing."

As the young Umbulala was endeavouring to get his mind round this latest wonder and calm himself all in the same breath, there and then, as if to demonstrate it, the Matriarch trundled off - and without the remotest outward sign of communication, the other elephants followed one by one.

"Mother nature…"

Ingwe crooned as they filed by like giant phantoms in the gauzy half-light,

"misses nothing. Take those grassy beds scattered about the ground in which each elephant slept....",

she beckoned the cubs towards large, flattened patches of earth, increasingly visible as the mist began to slowly dissipate in the growing warmth of morning,

"where the breaking up and levelling of the vegetation lets the light in to give birth to new growth. The sun only needs to rise twice before the shoots have shot up just enough to attract grazing animals - knowledge"......

Ingwe purred pointedly at spotted and black cub in turn,

"wise hunters will use to their advantage. In its way, it's akin to the work of Brother fire when, after sweeping through the jungle, life quickly returns under the nurture of Brothers sun and wind and the caress of Sister rain. Remember...."

Ingwe urged them, scratching an itchy spot under her jaw,

"everything, however seemingly small or ordinary, has a purpose."

She must have caught a nerve, and Umbulala's fond remembrance of the trembling ripples, tumbling down her sleek coat and back again, was as fresh as Ingwe's lesson of the elephant beds and the message of the whistling thorn flooding back to him down the breadth of seasons.

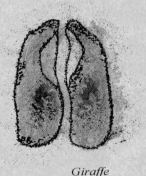

Giraffe

BY TOOTH AND CLAW

The leaf has as much in design as the flower

One uninvited encounter with leopard was sufficient for one season; another in as many moons, as Umbulala might surmise from the standpoint of the responsible professional, verged on the careless. It all unfolded shortly after sun-up. With a hint of insouciance lightly investing his step the panther had been casually sauntering along, wending his way slowly toward the fringes of his territory, unhurried and unperturbed by any plan, or need to be somewhere in particular. Quite simply he was enjoying the luxury of a nonchalant ramble at an easy, gracious pace through the last of the plateau country; before the bronze and orange-gold splash of its rolling swell of Musasa trees dropped away to the riverine tracts marking the boundary of his range. Here all was different: a weave of Mahogany, Waterberry and Ebony trees, Strangler Figs, reeds and multi-branched Doum palms mingling in a rich amalgam of greens lifted, just now and then, by the luminous flash of a Fever tree winking brightly from a riverbank, or from the isolated splendour of its hermit-perch on a rockface.

The panther had been ambling nonchalantly along, appropriately vigilant, yet not overly expectant of anything untoward. It was his home territory after all; territory over which he had well and truly established dominance. Hence when the strong scent of male leopard suddenly assailed his nostrils, it was as unexpected as it was disturbing. Along with other sign, the scent had been growing stronger with every step, until finally reaching alarming heights at the base of a fruiting tree - a landmark, otherwise prominent for being the sole representative of its kind for some distance round. Its other natural distinction was an appealing bounty of berries; an ambrosial lure marking it out as a veritable honeypot, the ground under it strewn with half-eaten fruit, twigs and leaves attesting to its attraction. As such it was major a focal point for a flow of foraging fauna.

Nothing could have sent a stronger signal to Umbulala. Another leopard was challenging for his territory. No predator so blatantly marks a pivotal place of forage - and good hunting - as it will scare off the game being attracted to the fodder. There had to be at work here a deeper, darker design. As there wasn't a chance such a popular foraging point would go unmissed, or unvisited, by the resident leopard, the intruder could only have left his scent and sign among the innocent sprinkling of discarded and fallen foliage and berries with deliberate intent. Spraying, marking and scraping the ground and trunk in that signature way of male leopard sent a calculated challenge that was unmissable, and unequivocal.

For Umbulala it wasn't a case of alternatives; a case of some leopard straying by accident into his territory and, by virtue of that, not harbouring any devious motive or determination. This intruder came down on the devious intent side, without question. All the indications were there. As such there could be no half measures. Utmost caution must be Umbulala's mentor, as one thing was certain. If the outcome of an encounter amounted to a head-to-head conflict it would be all or nothing - death for one, or both. Either way, the panther had no choice. He must set out at once to track down, stalk and see off, by tooth and claw if need be, this brash intruder who could so rashly make a claim on Umbulala's domain.

Crouched low, Umbulala slipped on through the scrub, heading for a stony hummock conspicuous up ahead above the bush. Taking advantage of every shadow cast, every play of dark on light, the black cat shimmied and slithered with infinite care. He'd just come up to the rear of it - a rocky heap projecting straight up from the ground - when a breeze delivered a whiff of the intruder's scent right to his waiting nostrils. From here, relatively shielded by some fallen rubble, he checked the skyline above the upper rocks for the tell-tale bump sticking up - a head neatly outlined against the blue. Some animals fail to resist the urge to peer out over the rim of a kopje or other high promontory, rather than sideways round some protecting shield of cover, and in so doing give themselves away. But the panther had a hunch this intruder was no such fool. He crept on round the base of it, before nosing in under a heavy overhang of foliage which, in linking up with a clutter of shrubs and creepers had formed a deflective screen in a veiled, latticework of greenery. Thus camouflaged behind this deceptive innocence of leaf and bough, Umbulala caught sight of the foe.

A large, spotted leopard was peering from the crest of an anthill. At some distance up a dry riverbed trailing away to the back of the termite mound - and with all the makings of adding an intriguing twist - a troop of baboons was moving ever steadily closer. Neither troop nor spotted leopard looked, as yet, to be aware of the other. Not so the leopard of Umbulala. As if Mother nature had figuratively tapped the intruder on the shoulder he'd partially turned his head in the direction of the panther's hide. The one eye Umbulala could see appeared to be studying every detail of where the black cat was concealed; an eye with a seemingly supernatural ability that gave every impression of being able to focus with such intensity, Umbulala was sure he could be seen; an eye he didn't doubt could even pick out the ants trailing along the twigs above his head.

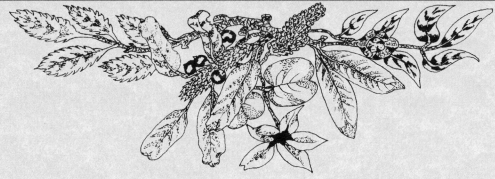

Just then, with another turn of the spotted head, the intruder's secret was out. He was blind in the other eye. A vicious, raw-looking scar - one that could only have been inflicted by the swingeing swipe of a dew claw - ran down from the brow, over the eye to the cheek. Umbulala pondered the possibilities of such an injury, possibly the result of a fearful scrap some moons back with another leopard, maybe even lion. Yet, as Umbulala's every instinct urged him, even a skerrick of sympathy for this leopard would be wildly out of place. Here was one formidable cat. Merely to survive in the jungle with such a disability, let alone reach this cat's size, proved the scar-faced leopard was no less the leopard for it. Moreover, nature is never so heartless not to compensate for such injuries, and this is invariably by enhancing one or other of the senses - in this instance probably the good eye for starters!

While now convinced this unwelcome intrusion into his territory was no accident, Umbulala wasn't in a rush. Big cats, only too aware how deadly their claws and teeth are, will prefer to avoid face-to-face combat with a rival; especially one of similar looking mien or ability. A few, brief skirmishes to allow the bigger or more intimidating aggressor scope to show off its size and strength is usually sufficient; the smaller or lesser contender taking the line of least resistance and backing off. But this leopard didn't remotely look the backing-off type! On this basis Umbulala reckoned his best option would be a surprise attack off the intruder's blind side. With strategy thus decided, the panther was all but ready to break cover when, in that way of fate and fortune, the unexpected stumbled clumsily on the scene. Upriver a lone dog baboon suddenly bolted from the woodland headlong into the troop. Hurling itself at the leader in brutal abandon, the humdrum at once degenerated into pandemonium.

Baboons scattered like bats from a cave, *waughing* and bawling wildly as antagonist and alpha male mauled, rolled and tumbled into a raucous bruising brawl. As mayhem erupted behind, scar-face swung his head in the direction of the uproar. Turning at an angle from which he could follow it with his good eye, the spotted cat quickly rose up on his back legs in a half-crouched position to witness the scrap better. It was a fateful decision. While sharp instinct had earlier warned him there might be something lurking about with a bead on him, Brother error had since skipped about in his mind. With concentration broken, the moment was set. Umbulala recognized his chance.

Narrowing the distance to the termite mound in a shimmer, Umbulala drew his paws up under him, and with every sinew tensed, leapt up and on to the scar-faced leopard in one. He knew he must slay his opponent swiftly, or himself be the bearer of terrible wounds; worse, be killed.

On impact the big spotted cat sprang into the air, turning full somersault in the process - an amazing feat of strength that, with the full weight of the panther on his back, attested to the intruder's mettle. But Umbulala's teeth were already ramming into his challenger's neck at the critical point just below the skull, crucially preventing the spotted cat retaliating with his own awesome fangs. Umbulala knew just what was needed. While all four paws of vicious, hooked claws raked down the intruder's flanks and back, digging and ripping away at hide and flesh, Umbulala's jaw muscles worked relentlessly as he drove his canines deeper and deeper between the spotted cat's vertebrae to snap its backbone in one, bone-wrenching stroke.

The big scar-faced cat died as he hit the dust. Shaking the body from side to side, Umbulala was still agrip by the neck; only when convinced it was broken did he release his hold and let the carcass slide to the ground. He quickly glanced up the dry river bed - there wasn't a baboon in sight. He could hear his heart thumping, his sides bellowing in and out as if his ribcage might explode outwards. As with any jungle fracas the ubiquitous hush that heralds, then holds it in thrall, choked the air - broken only at strife's end by an alleluia of birdsong and insect tremolo bursting up to quicken the heart, and trill tales of the rout round the treetops. Across the riverbed baboons, utterly transfixed, had been gauping from hastily seized vantage points in the tall Ebony trees; trees fondly known hereabouts as *Jackalsberry,* due to the appeal of their fruit to sweet-toothed jackals. They'd been close to *two* rancorous full-grown male leopards, and as a few openly trembled, one loudly barked out:

"The scar-faced leopard is dead - killed by a *black* leopard!"

To Umbulala's bemusement those baboons who hadn't seen him - or couldn't believe something as 'aberrant' as a black leopard - protested as much in that raucous way of their kind. As it rapidly descended into the usual, rowdy shenanigans of baboons, the panther took advantage of the diverting rumpus to quietly, and very anonymously slip away. Shortly after, holed up in some welcome solitude seemingly a moon away from bawling, brawling baboons and prying eyes, he licked off the spoils of strife. Mentally picking over the events of earlier, he found himself recalling what, in his estimation, had to be a more terrifying encounter by far to witness.

It had occurred moons previously, down by a waterhole. Umbulala was stretched out on a grassy knoll, relaxed in the shade of a sweet-scented Violet tree overlooking the water. In spectacular bloom, its crown of fragrant, lilac-pink flowers alive with butterflies, bees and sunbirds, all was in harmony with the mood and the moment. Umbulala luxuriated in a cooling bed of wild chives as he enjoyed a panoramic view of the comings and goings at the waterhole; a leopard's delight all in one. He remembered the bliss of rolling in the aromatic

grass as he lazily surveyed the wider vista: the soothing throb of the encircling bush; a scattering of graceful waterbuck does browsing the clutter of scrub dotted with trees that rolled round the waterhole clearing; and dozing serenely under the leafy crown of one tree his clearest recollection of all - a Black rhino bull wearing the beatific expression of an animal without a troubled thought.

Umbulala had undying respect for these lumbering giants....of either type; a respect going back to adolescence and his first bruising encounter with the fiery Black rhino. The memory of it still chilled him with horror, setting him to ponder on the potential for misrule that might prevail if rhinos preferred thicker jungle to more open country, with leopards probably becoming virtual tree dwellers, like monkeys, as a result. And Umbulala hissed between his teeth at the mere notion of any such comparison between himself and a monkey. Just then, bubbling with an ebullience for life and all things living, a diminutive elephant calf toddled out from behind some scrub; a harmless enough event offering no threat to anything, was the panther's confident summation. Oh how readily a self-assured assumption can be turned on its head. What next occurred not even the wisest observer of life and it's creatures could have predicted.

Suddenly one uncoordinated baby elephant, all flappy ears and dangly snout flopping about - disjointed disarray on-the-loose - darted over to the dozing bull where an inquisitive trunk was indelicately poked with an audible snuffle into an inviting ear. It was a probe too far. Besides a black rhino's ears being sacrosanct - hearing is their prime sense - from the bull's standpoint it must have been akin to being dumped on by a breaker of chilly, foaming surf. In an instant the massive animal was up on his great padded feet and steaming out from under the tree, puff-snorting and fuming in a haze of dust and grit churned up in the motion. Startled rudely to his nonplussed senses, the fractious Black rhino was back in the land of the sentient with a vengeance!

What immediately followed was an object-lesson on how fate, with its crude

sense of timing, so recklessly holds life to ransom. At the precise moment - not a hairs-breath either side - the herd Matriarch strolled from behind the cover of greenery hitherto blocking her view of the waterhole, she wandered right into the path of the tiny calf rushing for its life from the rhino storming after it. Unstoppable in its course, the little elephant's route to salvation took it between the Matriarch's legs, in under her belly and out the other side - with thundering up at full momentum from behind the rhino on course for a broadside with the Matriarch. With a rhino's eyesight being the weakest of its senses, all the unfortunate bull could register at such close quarters was a pall of grey. That was enough.

Thrusting his head up, he plunged his formidably solid front horn full into the Matriarch's flank as far as it would go, with the force of the thrust so great, the rhino's smaller rear 'sleeper' horn impacted. The cow shuddered ominously. The long horn penetrated upwards into her heart and she trumpeted wildly in agony. Incredibly, by the time the rhino had withdrawn his horn and was attempting another headlong assault, the Matriarch was ready for him. She neatly side-stepped the charge, and with a twist of her head and a swift lunge forward and down, rammed her tusks at full tilt into his side, tossing him a

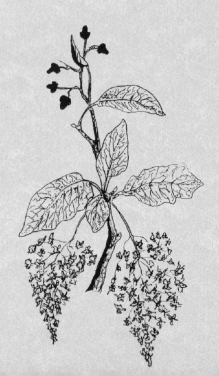

buffalo length into a sprawl of thornbush. Somehow the rhino landed on his feet. Rocking and shaking he remained upright in defiance of logic, his bloody, horn-encrusted head hung low, glaring fire at the other giant. An eternity seemed to stretch by; then all at once the rhino faltered - after which his demise was rapid, and unalterable.

His powerful legs were the first to give way; they crumbled, he sank to the ground -

then with a sigh, and none the wiser for his going, all life, that once indomitable flame of being, ebbed from his body. As for the elephant Matriarch, she fared no less better considering she hadn't the remotest chance of understanding what had brought it all to pass. Suddenly attacked by a rhino in a fireball of fury, her instinct had been to retaliate and defend her own. With one tusk now broken - embedded in the rhino - she staggered and thrashed about, crashing into trees and bushes. Then, like the rhino before her, she too began to falter and stumble. One moment she was upright; next her legs just fell away from under her. Sinking onto her rear she rapidly succumbed, slipping down and over in a mighty crash, the cloud of dirt and grit thrown up in the fall fanning out like a dusty shroud.

For Umbulala, just at what moment they materialized was lost in the mists of memory. All he could recall was the entire area coming alive with elephants teeming about - wildly stamping and trumpeting, before milling en masse round the dead Matriarch. Calm enveloped the waterhole as each elephant in turn went through the ritual motions of sniffing, touching and gently prodding the motionless body with their trunks: first tentative, then more inquiring, progressing to encouraging, yet still deferential caresses, then finally bolder nudges intended to rouse her. Many attempts to lift her followed. To no avail. Thereafter something quite extraordinary unfolded. The herd proceeded to enact what to all intents and purposes was a solemn ceremony of last rites - how it looks to any thoughtful observer - which the panther wouldn't have believed if he hadn't seen it with his own eyes.

With much purpose and precision, the elephants started breaking branches off the trees and bushes about them, taking care the foliage remained intact. They went on to lay each leafy cluster over the body, bunching them together until the body of the dead Matriarch was cloaked reverentially in what appeared no less than what it looked like: a floral, funerary drapery of green. Even more remarkable, they next did the same for the rhino. Only when both had been formally covered in this way did a significant swearing-in take place: another elephant assumed the mantle of leadership - a female of course, probably the Matriarch's eldest daughter. When all was done the herd turned; then in unison, as if by some unuttered directive meant for the understanding of elephants only, slowly plodded away, a departure made all the more memorable for it being silhouetted in the spiritual balm that is the tropic sky at sunset - a glorious rose-gold panorama as constant to sunrise, as moon is to stars, birth is to death.

The panther watched them go, all lightheartedness fled, a confused and sober soul in an agony of wonder over how something so innocent could grow so irredeemably, so unwittingly, into something so terrible. Brother error rampant, or just the terrible beauty of life at work for which, as some would have it, there are no given reasons, no winners, just senseless waste. And as he dwelled on this, he looked up to see a strangely reassuring pattern of winged specks circling the sky - and found cause to humbly reconsider.

Lion

MESSENGERS ON THE WING

Even the cicada has a song to sing

T he wind wheeled and whistled its way through a web of jungle and bush on its long flight down from the highlands, twisting the damp foliage this way and that as it winged by in gentle swells one moment, strong breezes the next. Born among the icy peaks and ravines of the equatorial mountains way up country, it whipped across the chill, upper ramparts gathering pace, thence out over the rolling panoply of wilderness beyond. Sweeping away along the winding ridges of the rift escarpment through lush forests and choking jungle, thence down to the lowlands over meandering woodland - and scrub savanna that gradually gave on to rolling grasslands - it changed mood at every level as it cheekily flitted about leaf and branch like some wild, wood sprite. It swung on through Umbulala's territory, carrying on it varied scents and sounds - including, this day, that of the Kori bustard.

The regal progress of a tall, long-necked Kori strutting unhurriedly through the open bush, crested head held high, is unmistakable. Among the heaviest of flying birds, it's a reluctant flyer and thus largely earthbound. With a superior air as it nonchalantly promenades, rather than walks, of one never rushed or fazed, the Kori is more or less unique unto itself. Yet for all the aura of stately reserve, in its courtship display a Kori cock will inflict upon itself a near paroxysm of flagellatory torment, in any number of body contortions, as it flaunts and prances about outrageously in front of a desirable hen. Stretching itself tall and stiff, it flips its outspread tail up against its back, erecting its body feathers and those around its neck into a great white puff that all but engulfs its head. Now looking as if it's been turned inside out, it proceeds to sashay from side to side alluringly, courting appreciative glances, before halting again in rigid pose - all the better to be admired and studied - while letting forth with a booming call that can penetrate any repose. It appears to work: such an exhibitionist spectacle, in company with the rolling base-drum *woum-woum-woumooumm* of the Kori's mating song, apparently so besots a Kori female that they mate - so much for stately reserve - on the spot!

"All very well for Kori bustards...." Umbulala's thoughts fizzled through a drowsy haze.

He'd been snoozing peacefully beneath the cover of a favourite tree - until the Kori pair showed up. When not in anyway connected it can be extremely vexing - the penetrating "boom boom" beat of an enthused cock's love lilt boring into the subconscious like a determined termite. Now aroused from slumber, the panther blinked sleepily from his leafy perch. The big bird was now dancing attendance on a prospective mate just beyond a flat, spreading slab of granite, which, after some long past activity deep in the earth, had metamorphosed into a surface outcrop, weathering over time to a grey-green mantle of rock flecked with mica crystals that gleamed and winked in the sunlight. Umbulala's hooded eyes flicked across the scene: the odd, strangely elegant birds that looked forever old, and the ancient rock glistening in the sharp light. He stretched along the branch; then keeping his balance in check while taking care not to draw attention to himself, rose up on all fours on the smooth skin of bark that wrapped it. What can be best described as the unsuspecting unwittingly bidden awake - courtesy of the Kori cock - Umbulala wasn't altogether unpleased; it didn't do for any predator of standing to sleep away too much of the day. Slipping imperceptibly down the shadowed side of the trunk, in just a few strides he'd melded into the web of undergrowth flanking the clearing, silent and featherlight of trace as is the mark of the cat of whatever make.

A little distance on he stopped at a shady rock pool to refresh and invigorate his palate, juiceless as a shed husk from his earlier nap. The pool was invitingly positioned in the shelter of a towering boss of gnarled rock. Umbulala lapped with slow, studied pleasure savouring every vestige, casting his head back to allow the cooling trails to tickle alive his taste buds and glissade down his throat to revitalize him from the inside. The panther's tongue glowed healthily rose-pink against the black of his hide. In the regular course of tossing back his head Umbulala would cast a quick eye around. In

so doing he picked up on something rather odd - there was not a hint of wind about. The panther lifted his head high, cupping his ears to catch the tiniest sound on their fine down of sensory, vibrissae-like hairs. He thrust his snout out, flaring his nostrils wide to sniff long and hard at the air, drawing in deep draughts to locate a breeze. But there was nothing; and with nothing, no scents or sounds to be deciphered. It was puzzling: one moment the wind would be blowing a veritable gale - with all the racket and every pong of the jungle no creature with a modicum of taste could want thrust down their ears, or up their nostrils - and usually when he didn't welcome the invasion; another moment, as now, when he sought the same for reasons of good bushcraft - not a whisper.

Something shivered in the shadows. Sharp feline eyes focused on a flitter-winged shape; presently a butterfly fluttering softly by set the thoughtful cat musing on a Mother nature who can nurture into existence such a diversity of life-forms, from the fierce and supremely huge all the way to the gentlest insect. But moments after he was humbly reconsidering home-spun theories about gentle insects, when a snatched glance of a preying mantis in the foliage brought vividly to mind the first time he saw a mantis devouring another. Somewhere in the midst of all this seemingly pointless rumination the panther was sure there had to be a reason - when, lo and behold, he at last detected a breeze, as if the butterfly's wings were generating it, and on the back of it a trace of a subtle whisper: *with caution little brotheerrr*. Umbulala reproached himself:

"Am I developing the brain of a Go-away bird? Was that the butterfly...."

he growled quietly to himself, "or the wind!"

The strange mutability of life conspiring to confuse. Umbulala endeavoured to concentrate. He knew something of the vicissitudes of life. He also knew how the jungle is neutral for hunter and hunted; how a move a mere hair's breadth either way can drop one right in the path of death. Mutability, life, death - these were notions to dampen the most up-beat spirit when not expected, and the best cure Umbulala knew for it was a change of scene.

The area of scrubby underbrush Umbulala had just passed through ran into a disorderly scramble of thornbush. An infamous menace long familiar to the panther as *wait-a-bit* scrub, its clutching hooked thorns scattered in pairs - where one misses, the other kicks in - will prick and cling tenaciously to skin or fur the more one hastily jerks and pulls away. As the name implies, it's a cool, steady approach that's called for when tackling *wait-a-bit*. Fortunately this patch was short-lived; directly beyond the ground opened onto a steep incline of gnarled granite that ran in a convenient spiral of terraces all the way up the slope to the long escarpment. The stony face was exposed full into the morning sun, glowing invitingly. Having cleared the thorn, the panther leapt directly onto the first ledge. The sudden burst of solar fire on his back melted all resistance; he rolled over, and with all four paws in the air and head thrown wantonly back in unrestrained abandon, Umbulala gave himself over to the seductive, smouldering warmth of sunlight on rock.

He found himself peering upwards and backwards at an overhanging remnant of the *wait-a-bit* with, perched on a stem of it like a tiny sliver of sky dropped to earth, a little Blue waxbill. In a flash Umbulala was a cub again, musing lightly on how very different life looked when viewed from upside down. Soon his eyes began to smart from the strain of the angle. Concluding it was better to view the earth right side up, he flipped back onto his belly just as the waxbill flitted down to the ledge at a spot just beyond his reach. She began to peck at a clutch of grass seeds blown there on the wind. Unperturbed by the panther's presence, the little bird fussed daintily about them, her lilac bill working over each morsel with infinite care. All done, she wiped its tip against the buff-brown feathers of one wing, and was puffing out her blue breast......when the quite unexpected happened. Turning toward the cat with an assuredness that belied her size, a sound, rather like a tinkling rattle, floated over to a singularly unprepared panther:

"Brother panther - Hairless ape are on the rampage!"

When those brief interludes in life, made significant by the deliciousness of giving ourselves over completely to the joy of a moment lose their innocence, we're never ready. As now. No wind blew, yet here on the air hung a grim message of foreboding, unsought and uninvited, meant just for him. Was it the wind conveying it - odd, as there was none about - or the waxbill! Strange mutability indeed. Just then, resolution came as the tiny snip of sky called again:

"My kin watched them ransack the nests of the Green pigeons in the Fig groves of the far forest."

A bemused panther tried to gather himself, a muddle of questioning thoughts yelling in his head. Why was he hearing this? What could be behind it? Worse,

with dawning realization, what clandestine plot was afoot with him, the ingenue, at the centre of it! With dawning realization comes awakening. Curiosity - that abiding quality never ultimately extinguished by difficulty or accident of fortune - had begun to win over confused wonder. But bemusement is a reluctant leave-taker and Umbulala shook his head to free himself of dread suspicion, and tentatively, hesitantly, crooned inquiringly back:

"How......how many, little sister?"

More inquisitiveness than shocked surprise now driving his thinking, a relieved Umbulala was functioning again. Though he was still none the wiser, the deadly duo of confusion and doubt didn't sit well on him; indeed on anyone - one feeding off the other to the point that nothing is achieved but inertia.

"As many as there are toes on the front of my foot" the waxbill twittered enigmatically in return, fluttering back up to the thornbush. Alighting again on a stem, Umbulala's eye immediately fell on one of two tiny feet clenched round it: *three* - there were three of them. He learned from the waxbill how one was very wise - wise like the jungle and smells like the jungle, sees all, misses little; who before reaching the place of the buffaloes scents them and avoids them; one who can even call to guineafowl in their own tongue, and with just a sapling and some bark catch them 'for the bellies of hairless ones to feed on.' Just then, at the beckoning *weet-a-weet* call of another waxbill she flew off, leaving Umbulala alone with his thoughts.

He lounged on in the sun, recalling the warnings of Ingwe, of Bulala his father, not least his own direct knowledge of hairless ape. They were dangerous foes. Thus with self-preservation uppermost, along with the wiser counsel of hard experience lending its own heavyweight support, the big cat concluded there was but one course open to him: to put as much distance between himself and the hairless ones until they returned to their territory in the grasslands. And without hesitation he rose, his intention to head for the remotest and deepest parts he knew. It was a journey of at least two sunrises, which would take him far up country, through changing vistas and climes, on into jungle tracts he hadn't ventured to in a long while.

No more aptly observed than as a rolling bounce on padded springs of paws, perfectly proportioned to suppress any sounds of passage, the measured gait of an adult leopard with resolve - trailed by a tail like a horizontal question mark -

is never anything but that of a cat going somewhere. The panther made good headway, covering a fair stretch of terrain. A sunset came and went, and still he was comfortable with his decision: a sojourn in remote, denser reaches was more than satisfying to his senses. To begin with there would be fewer major predators, notably that of lion; a lot less of those irksome wild dogs; hyaena too. And as he skipped through a mental checklist of pluses, his thoughts ran to others he'd be less likely to encounter in thicker cover: vultures and their ilk for one, creatures he wouldn't miss in a rash of moons, the jungle configuration of where he was heading being too enclosed for such open country habitués. Musing thus, yet infinitely careful not to lose focus or let his mind wander off track, Umbulala continued at a trim pace, determined nothing should distract or deflect him from his goal. But he hadn't counted on fate: as always, more determined. Without a solitary moment of warning an urgent, very commanding bark exploded from the

vegetation about him:

"*Cat of the night:* deliver death's sweet bite and free me from this torment!"

Cutting the air like an icy blast, the alarming desperation of that chill plea, the distress call of an animal in extremis, took his breath away. Jolted to a standstill by its abruptness, Umbulala quickly rallied his senses. Falling into a crouch and tucking his paws under him in one deft movement, he readied himself to leap or run, whatever should be demanded. With a surreptitious sweep of his eyes he checked about him. Everywhere a maze of wood and leafage hung thick and heavy, reducing his field of vision to just a few buffalo lengths in any direction. So too the silence; so heavy was it even the beat of droplets of moisture off frond and twig, usually barely audible, was like the pumping of blood in his ears. In spite of the palpable tenseness, Umbulala relaxed limbs and muscles stretched taut as sinew; just enough to ease the thumping of his heart, but not dull or lessen his reflexes or speed of reaction.

Emboldened for being the more composed, he now cast longer, more lingering glances wider afield. Again he couldn't find sight or sound of a living animal - until, after what seemed an agony of moons, an arrestingly handsome form merged slowly into perspective from behind a deceiving web of vegetation. Heaviest and most brightly liveried of the forest antelopes, there stood in the shadowy arbour, hitherto hidden by its lush cover, was a magnificent bongo bull luminous mid the well of greenness - indeed, in its burnished hide of vibrant chestnut boldly striped in white, the antelope appeared almost aflame. It seemed improbable one could miss it. The black leopard scrutinized the antelope's face for surface wounds, and other giveaways to injury in a laboured twitch or tic. But only the melancholy cast of the eyes - with more of a watery glaze than is fitting in the fully alive - kept drawing him back. The panther let slip a cavilling snarl:

"Mighty Bongo - why deliberately seek death when there is all to live for in

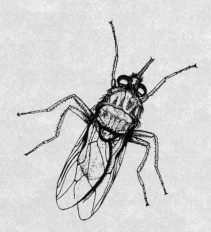

Mother earth's jungle?"

The bull didn't flinch, remaining fearlessly upright, head high, raw nature in all its splendour:

"Hairless apes have struck me…." it rasped "and now I'm fodder for the parasites that sup and gnaw at my flesh. I can do naught to stop them, and I crave the quick death the great panther brings."

At that the bongo lurched fully into view - and a sight met Umbulala's eyes for which he was in no way prepared. Dragging behind the bull's still robust torso and flanks were two lifeless hindlegs, scarred and eaten away, each a gruesome relic of a trap. But not a trap woven of bark, skin nor vine from which there's a sporting chance of escape. Rather a trap fashioned of an unnatural substance not of the jungle; so strong it couldn't be broken by such a powerfully-built animal. In the bongo's efforts to free itself, an insidious strip of fence wire - born of the seemingly innocuous cattle barrier, accursed bequest of the alien world to wild places and their inhabitants - had sliced deeper and deeper through the bongo's hide and flesh. Halting eventually at bone, its final, damning duty was to leave the antelope's hindquarters to waste away, alive only with maggots and flesh-flies. The big buck blinked, and Umbulala was in motion. Little more than a blur, he struck - and in a single bite released the ailing bongo from its enforced agony. The panther lifted up his head as if to howl at the skies, but instead let out a screaming roar into the wind:

"Let Mother nature know of the bongo's courage", it trenchantly rang out "and curses upon those that can so treat another animal!"

Just then a breeze picked up and began to blow gently about the panther's ears:

"This have I done little brother…." it seemed to whisper back in kind "to wit I brought messages your way, aided even by Sister butterfly….but you couldn't have been concentrating!"

Umbulala grunted in exasperation:

"You must have had your paw in your mouth...."

shaking his big head in disbelief,

"as I heard nothing clearly until Sister waxbill, then my own intuition warning me to take myself off to remoter cover. Messages....." he spluttered with fierce intent into the breeze "on *butterfly* wings no less! Just where does fooling around stop and your famous diligence begin?!"

Umbulala was pleased with his little rebuff. But it clearly missed its mark as faithful wind whistled mildly back, too long experienced in the moods of the jungle and its creatures to be perturbed by any such jibes:

"Soooo.....pray tell this humble servant of Mother nature where the mighty panther might be going, and in such agitated mood? Is this not the cat that strikes fear in all?"

Umbulala grimaced, coughing back sharply, the hairs on his back bristling:

"Doing what the wind has always taught him to do - obey wiser counsel and leave the hairless ones alone. They'll soon get bored struggling about the depths of the jungle fighting off Brother and Sister tsetse fly, and their kin the mosquitoes! It's quite simple. The insects on their own will rid us of them, and all we have to do meantime is make ourselves scarce."

With that the greenery all around Umbulala began to flap and flail about with such a force, it was as if something compelling was about to be announced.

"Cat of the night...."

it appeared to command,

"Mother earth has sought the help of Mother nature in a mission of urgency. And you can wriggle like that snake of tree and shrub, the wily boomslang, but it is upon you the task has fallen; on you - the chosen one. Mock and be facetious as you wish....."

it seemed to chide with increasing intensity, forcing the panther to half-close his eyes and set his jaws against it,

> "but *don't* underestimate the hairless ones for all their apparent frailty; especially the old one crowned with white hair - the one slower than the rest who, as indeed you heard tell from Sister waxbill, is twice the hunter the others are. The jungle....."

it blew a gentle assurance

> "will be with you!"

Such blatant coercion rattled the panther rigid. As the wind dropped, he opened his eyes wide. Wagging his head sharply as if to shake off some unwanted phantasm, he knitted his eyebrows in that way of cats and hissed:

> "Mission? Chosen one? As Brother sun sinks into a slumber I could be far away, Sister moon my only guide, in a thick of jungle where I can live off tree hyrax and monkeys for moons too numerous to come!!"

The wind moaned back as the panther threw himself down onto the ground, groaning and thrashing his tail about petulantly like an unrepentant offspring at odds with a higher authority:

> "They are far from their normal surroundings, penetrating deep into jungle spaces where Mother nature fears they'll work more havoc."

Umbulala flicked onto his belly, giving himself a vigorous shake, and twitching his ears agitatedly as if refusing to hear what came next:

> "They must be stopped. As you're heading in the general direction, Mother nature has accorded you the privilege."

Resistance was doing him little good - but he hadn't given up the fight. Nodding bitterly, the big cat sprang up onto his haunches:

"In that *general* direction; apart from which I'm presumed to take it that there's no one else dim enough to stop them.....except Umbulala! You may not know it *Wind*...."

he spat belligerently

"but life in the jungle is not easy, so why should I go out of my way to face injury and probable annihilation! You seem a better friend of Brothers error and death than of me!"

The cat fumed resentfully. Sat-stood there, immovable as a rock, a light wind whirled relentlessly about him. Umbulala was not amused, snarling softly under his breath. Protest, however, was becoming futile and a hint of resignation began to creep across his face.

"'Tis not true hunter of the night....."

the panther thought he heard a cajoling breeze rustle back through the foliage,

"for the jungle is a neutral place as I have long coached you; the wise walk with care, while the foolish and over-confident meet with Brother error, or death. Thus..."

on it played enticingly, in and out the leaves and about his ears

"has Mother nature sought out the wise and courageous to defend her jungle. You *have* this gift of wisdom...."

it whistled seeming inducements about his head, appearing to coax and urge him on in what now truly smacked of nothing less than raw coercion,

"*and* resourcefulness, a fitting combination in the face of hairless apes. All the jungle will aid you. You're far behind, and they've worked much mischief already."

The breeze dropped to a teasing whisper among the leaves. But the leopard is a creative cat, and Umbulala's face brightened; he still wasn't ready to give up the

struggle in this battle of wits:

"Noooo - *not* wise, courageous, resourceful, but instead....." a disgruntled cat snorted back "try dumb, gullible and full of bluster as that's the true interpretation of all this flattery being heaped on me. *Well* seek no further! Clearly no one is better equipped for this expedition than lion; and not Sister lion, but *Brother* lion! Bigger and meaner than me, boastful, pumping enough bluster to equip a troop of baboons, and ready to take on anything - in short, strutting vanity on four paws."

And as such just the one to set on hairless apes, so ran Umbulala's tongue-in-cheek reasoning.

"Whhyyy....."

the black cat smarmed on, squirming inwardly at how he could play the unctuous toady with such ready ease

"perhaps I should seek Brother lion out with the suggestion, while you relax back in the clouds."

Umbulala's face veritably glowed with the brilliance of his marvellous idea. But Wind would have none of it.

"Umbulala....."

a breeze whipped fiercely about him,

"it is you! Lion is simply too strident, big and clumsy for climbing all those interminable rockfaces and trees. Nor is he enough of a loner, or as readily able to create strategies on his own without the aid of a phalanx of wiser Sister lions. Not only that: Brother lion is simply too absorbed with Brother lion to bring himself to seek assistance from others if the need should arise, and as such is just completely wrong for the task. Go about it with good heart and grace Umbulala - *mighty* panther......"

a persistent wind blew in and out the leafage as if to urge him on

"who eats the hearts of lions, and smites the wild-dog pack. Here is verily an adventure you can't avoid - and must tackle with fervour."

The breeze that had been hitherto blowing briskly around Umbulala abruptly dropped, every leaf, twig, frond of grass bereft of movement. In rhythm with the swing of mood Umbulala pondered awhile, sitting quietly in the stillness. He turned to look at the dead bongo and growled softly: there was just no way out, nothing for it but to accept his fate. And taking a long, deep breath he let out a resigned sigh. He gazed at the carcass, the massive horns and handsome striped coat conspicuous in the broken vegetation where it had fallen. Most striking of all was the boldness of the stripes against the hide, and it put Umbulala in mind of another distinctive, striped creature he'd encountered long ago in the lower woodlands. This one was indeed unique.

He'd been reclining up a tall forest Teak tree at the time. Under the lush cover of its crown - a lacy tracery of pink petals and dark green - he was stretched flat along a branch swinging boldly out over a patch of scrub. Above the broken canopy of the cool, woodland forest the sun was about to set mid an array of clouds awash in a flush of rose and coral. Off in the near distance an impala ram was busy corralling his does. All seemed oblivious to the panther shadowed in the tree's rich spread of flower and foliage - as they were of another big cat steadily working its way toward them. From his prime vantage point Umbulala watched the cat utilize every fall and slant of cover to move increasingly closer the herd. Already recognizing the approaching hunter as a cheetah, it wasn't long before he realised its angle of movement would take the cheetah directly under the Teak tree. Dismissing the impalas from mind his thoughts verily buzzed:

"I'll have that cheetah...." readying himself for attack "and rid my territory of another competitor in the process!"

As the gap between quickly narrowed Umbulala was suddenly thrown by the cat's appearance. It was darker than usual. Where there should have been small spots there were great, heavy blotches unlike that of any cheetah he'd seen, irregularly shaped and very black. Yet still it moved with all the unmistakable grace of cheetah. Unfortunately this diverting distraction was losing the panther valuable advantage: put off track by such an unexpected twist, the cheetah was near enough passing by below. To compensate Umbulala quickly re-adjusted his position. Swiftly flicking his head and shoulders from one side of the tree limb to the other, he prepared to drop on the cheetah, now directly beneath. But something put him off; an obstacle in his line of vision. In the gap between there appeared to be several parallel branches blocking the way; branches that weren't there moments before. Thick as impala horns they ran the length of the cheetah, and Umbulala's reaction was to wait until the cat had moved out from under them.

A moment's hesitation was enough. In a couple of strides the cheetah was too far to be bushwhacked in a single clean drop from the tree. With any element of surprise gone wanting, Umbulala would have to streak down the trunk and make after a now alerted cheetah and attack on foot. He reasoned this to be a fairly questionable exercise, given how cheetahs can accelerate in a trice. An irked panther sniffed under his breath, involuntarily letting loose a cough that had the undesired effect of startling the impala herd into flight. In one smooth body they erupted in a whirling arabesque of springing vaults and high jumps unequalled in the wild,

clearing with consummate ease trees and bushes the height and girth of giraffes and elephants in a dash for their lives.

The tell-tale cough encapsulated it in one. The presence of a leopard was problem enough; when they saw the striped cheetah it was compounded. A leopard in a tree a little distance off is one thing; cheetah in close proximity quite another. To appear bigger and more threatening the latter had raised its neck ruffle and fur in response; it was equally on guard, what with the sound of leopard so near and the scrubland erupting in a riot of fleeing impalas more or less simultaneously. But this cat was no beginner, that much he recognised. While it's never prudent for a cheetah, however substantial, to tangle with such masters of camouflage as leopards - leopards hunt and kill cheetahs when chance allows - there existed every possibility of it making a renewed attempt on the impala herd later. So the striped cat took the better option: it sprinted effortlessly off....in the general direction of the retreating herd.

To Umbulala's way of thinking here was a cheetah who definitely knew a thing or two. Puzzling over the riddle of the branches that were there one moment, gone the next, he sizzled in silent indignation. It wasn't just the missed chance with the cheetah. His opportunity with the impala - the objective before the cheetah wandered uninvited into the frame - had also gone wanting, making it all the more galling. With his thoughts thus marooned in a self-pitying mire of question and regret, a sudden, jarring jolt in the tree, as if he were coming under attack from somewhere, startled Umbulala from his brooding reflections. Not so much alighting, as landing, the arrival of a cock Paradise whydah had rebounded violently along the branch.

It was a landing seemingly all over the place; yet it owed, not to any particular clumsiness on the bird's part, but to the sweeping cascade of long tail feathers cock whydahs develop in the mating season. Four times the size of normal, for such a handsome bird they can be the cause of a less than elegant landing. For all that a cock whydah in full breeding regalia is a knockout for a whydah hen, with striking black plumage set off to perfection by the yellow, white and tawny tricolour of its chest and belly feathers. Beyond an occasional sharp *chip,* they're not ones to verbalise much either. It's an odd contradiction - and one which frequently baffled Umbulala - that the stunners of the bird world should be endowed with voices verging on an often ear-splitting rasp, while plain, drab birds are the real purveyors of the wild's mellifluous songs and sounds. The compensatory wisdom of nature at work again. Hence it was as unexpected as surprising when the whydah directed a chirping whistle at the panther:

"With more appearing as the seasons pass that's the wonder of the jungle woodlands: the regal Striped cheetah, gifted with the best stratagem to grace nature in many a moon.....perfect *disruptive camouflage.* In place of spots it has bold, embossed stripes and blotches - the stripes running against convention along its back, instead of vertically down its flanks to neatly fool the likes of you, Brother panther!"

Indeed. A master of camouflage equal to any leopard, this Striped cheetah certainly did know a thing or two. Not for nothing would nature array it with what must be the pinnacle in camouflage coat markings to be found anywhere among larger land animals. Layered over creamy fur, a striking mix of unbroken black stripes running the length of its spine, and blotches of the same rich intensity swirling over the rest of it, adds up to a unique combination the cheetah could play off to perfection - defensively *and* offensively! And in the way of the best camouflage design, this scrubland cheetah's multi-patterned markings of stripes and blotches had the matchless effect of blending with foliage and branches to completely fool Umbulala in his leafy hide; likewise others of his ilk.

Leopards are the ultimate professionals; consummate predators who won't attack if the way isn't clear of obstructions that can prevent a clean strike. This cheetah's spinal stripes, seen from overhead by Umbulala as he peered down from the tree on the cheetah passing by below, would have broken up the striped cat's shape; and in the jumble of foliage and tension of the moment, readily look like branches in between. Any hunting leopard worth its mettle would delay attack - just enough for the cheetah to be too far for a direct hit in one. By contrast, a spotted cheetah would probably be dead and hanging ignominiously in Umbulala's favourite larder tree.

All these moons on, as he gazed on the bongo blessedly released of its ordeal, Umbulala could feel his hackles rising at the recollection. While to be fair he'd only ever encountered animals with stripes running *down* their bodies, like this bongo - and never together with blotches - he'd still been thoroughly fooled, as the whydah had so pointedly, and piquantly observed!

This *disruptive camouflage* of the majestic Striped cheetah was most surely a masterstroke; masterstroke enough to do him squarely out of a feast of impala, of that he was begrudgingly certain. Perhaps to clear it of all such nagging thoughts of the past, as much as the wearying misgivings attached to them, Umbulala shook his head, soundly rebuking himself for dwelling on striped cheetahs, bongos and the rest. Hairless apes should now be concentrating his mind.

And on this irrevocable turn of thought, he rose up on all fours and stretched long and lazily, as if to hold back the dread moment, that final severing of all ties with innocence which - despite his stoutest efforts at avoiding - still could be his fate. Then without further ado, lest doubt should again begin to fuss about his mind and heckle his senses, Umbulala struck out for the high jungle country where the rains are born: his ultimate destination its mysterious heart of tree-choked gorges, herb-covered meadows and boggy glades where - he'd heard it claimed, but couldn't yet begin to comprehend - misty peaks of fire and ice touch the clouds.

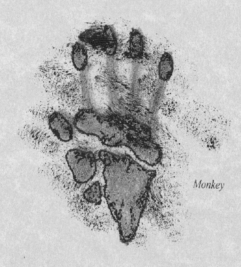

Monkey

TO THE RIFT ESCARPMENT

The vestments of nature, be they spotted,
dappled or striped, are never what they seem

et another golden sunrise was stretching its embrace around the dawn sky. Many had so broken along the horizon since the panther had set off on his long, snaking trek through the evergreen jungle, up into the moist mountain rainforests. This is the picturesque realm of great apes that leads on in turn to a filmy, misted sweep of high country, with its distinctive panorama of giant plants and icy peaks in imposing backdrop. Beyond the swathe of lower montane rainforest is the first of the hollow-stemmed bamboo. It girdles the high equatorial mountains in broad belts; on some actually marking the upper limit of the rainforest that characterizes the preferred habitat of the mountain gorilla. Growing in either solid stands, or scattered smaller clumps with intervals between, forest bamboo can reach upwards and more of a couple of giraffes placed head to hoof, with the bases of these tree-like grasses commonly as thick as the horns of eland.

Halted at the edge of it, the big cat was transfixed. The transition to bamboo can be abrupt or gradual, the pattern varying from place to place with altitude, prevailing winds, land features; even soil. Isolated stands of forest can grow scattered though the bamboo, with single tall trees towering above it all; stands of forest above the bamboo; or, perversely, patches of bamboo in the forest. Beginning above the bamboo belt is the giant heath, which on many of the equatorial mountains forms opalescent moorlands of quite transcendent beauty. Garlanded in streamers of wispy beard lichen, here flourish trees of heather taller than the tallest bamboo, with unfurling along the ground like a downy fleece, a mantle of gorgeously-hued moss. Harmonizing leaf-green through yellow and russet-gold, it runs over tree trunks, branches and rocks all the way up to the misty alpine region, the celestial sphere of giant, arborescent Groundsels and Lobelias - phantasmal plants no more than small herbs elsewhere - which stand like colossuses, and thrive in surreal stretches that spread up to the crater or snowline.

On other mountains there are intermediate bands of open, forested woodland between the bamboo and the giant heather. In grassy glades rugged in herbs and wildflowers, and superbly silhouetted against a setting of jungle-clad ravines and slopes, weirdly-shaped trees of unforgettable countenance dominate. Such was the country into which Umbulala had wandered. With massive trunks and stout branches flaring almost from their bases, huge Hagenia trees, hung with pendulous clusters of lilac coloured flowers, half-recline on the turf. Sharing the vista are slender Hypericums capped in bushy crowns of brilliant, yellow flowers dotted in a red mistletoe which gorillas are partial to. Everywhere  branches padded in furry nodules of moss are draped in ferns and vines and long gossamer trails of hanging lichen; while scattered through a mix of celery, blackberries and stands of stinging nettles the height of elephant grass, wildflowers bloom wherever sunlight breaks through.

Mountain rainforest differs from evergreen lowland forest primarily in the more moderate height of its trees, fewer lianas and a canopy that tends to be broken. More light is thus able to penetrate to the understorey, encouraging the blend of plant life that gives montane rainforest its character: ferns, climbers, flowering shrubs mixing in with non-fruiting bananas, and clumped-headed dracaenas rather like palm trees in miniature. While forest giants aren't as numerous as in the lower rainforests, statuesque specimens are still prominent, among them handsome Stinkwoods with plum-sized fruits - a further favourite of gorillas - and Podo trees, with spreading crowns and berries esteemed by birds and monkeys alike.

Such tracts sustain an array of animals, with elephant, gorilla, buffalo among the bigger game. Of others are splendid bongos in stretches, and chimps where gorillas are not; lovely ruddy-brown bushbuck; duikers of delicate-step and rufous hides that on occasion are black; bristled Giant forest hogs, massive and fearless; and tree-dwelling monkeys, agile and eye-catching, from flamboyant colobus, unmissable in a showy black-and-white livery, to long-tailed guenons such as dapper De Brazzas in smart white goatees, or shy, slender L'Hoests that scuttle about like genets, hooked-tip tails routinely upright; and, exclusive to the area where they favour its bamboo - moving out only to feed on forest vines or flowers - enchanting diademed Golden monkeys, most beautiful of their type.

By contrast to the relative openness of mountain rainforest, the tall stands of high altitude bamboo that generally encircle the equatorial mountains can be so densely tangled as to virtually exclude sunlight, permitting little in the way of understorey growth beyond ferns, fine grasses and mosses among a thick ground cover of shed leaves. Other than elephants - partial to feeding on the shorter "seedling" bamboo by browsing off the tops - only a limited number of animals make reasonable use of it; and those that do utilize it to full advantage through a combination of keen smell, hearing and agility. Golden monkeys can readily skim to safety up a slender bamboo stem; buffaloes will happily wile away a day in great clumps with alluring glades to graze; and while a reclusive bongo or a duiker will slip or dive with a semblance of grace through the densest thicket, elephant, buffalo and Forest hog just shove their way through with impunity.

UMBULALA

Despite the great quantities of grain bamboo produces - its seed head being like that of many other grasses - birds, other than some small seed-eaters, and francolins, aren't overly drawn to its eerie haven of rattling, moaning stems. With notable exceptions. Gazing up at this ultimate in grass, Umbulala was left with the fleeting impression of the shorter, tufted varieties familiar to him from the low country, especially in the way its spiky tops hang and wave in the wind. But here any similarity ends. This bamboo was strong enough to hold round its outer perimeter myriad globular nests, each a woven masterwork of fresh leaf strands slung on the outside of its upper stems and fronds like dangling melons. As for their gregarious, golden-feathered architects, the din of an entire working colony of weaver birds flying to and fro has to be heard. Umbulala wondered how they could possibly pay any heed mid such noisy hustle and bustle to a predator skulking about - ably put to the test when he strolled right up under them without a single bird calling out in alarm.

Of course what the little birds and the big leopard alike knew was that it would be pure fantasy for a cat the weight and size of Umbulala to reach them on the waving extremities of a frail fan of foliage. Yet it still seemed odd not to hear a startled call of warning above the clatter. He soon learned why. Beyond the chirpy prattle of industriousness were sounds peculiar to the bamboo; sounds such as those that follow its long-awaiting flowering when, after it sheds its seeds and dies, the tops snap off in the wind and the slowly-rotting stems begin to rattle and knock together. Leaving behind dry, hollow stalks into which a bevy of insects bore an indeterminate number of holes, eerier still is another sound characteristic of the bamboo at this twilight juncture in its life cycle. It's more regular in beat - and eminently more tuneful. A few bamboo stems will crack and crash to the ground. But most remain upright like great flutes, each stalk of giant grass transmogrified into a whistling reed through which the wind whirls bewitching tunes as it whines in and out the holes and hollow tops.

Away beyond the singing bamboo so engaging the panther's attention roved a vista of rare enchantment. A tapestry of colours, textures and shapes in total contrast to the closeted ranks of bamboo, a picturesque meadow of glades of intriguing trees - mid a rich assemblage of plants, herbs and wildflowers backlit by sunlight - sloped gently away toward a distant spectacle of green gullies and ravines. On between the clusters of giant nettles, blackberries and celery roiled lush swards of herbage picked through with lilies and violets, white and pink everlastings and the vermilion flashes of red-hot pokers. Conspicuous over all was the dreamlike spread of the trees. Ancient of aspect, each looked to have been moulded into shape by the winds of the high country, the fern bedecked limbs of some so bizarrely bent at haphazard angles, they lay virtually prostrate along the ground. Where branches, hung in feathery strands of lichen, weren't cocooned in pommels or wads of plush, green-gold moss, patches of yellowish fungi dappled the bark; just the crimson or chalk-white splash of orchids, winking in the exuberance, breaking the splendorous verdancy of it all.

For now the peculiar charm of the bamboo was sufficient to entrap the gaze of a wanderer from far-flung parts; indeed, Umbulala was having little compunction looking further. The towering mountain grass boasted sufficient of what was strange and new to occupy his curiosity, and it came as a welcome respite from his rapture of the senses when something familiar diverted his attention. It was a litter of fat piglets, one opportunistically on its own near a Groundsel, the tree's clustered ruffs of silver-green leaves glinting softly in the sunlight. Here in this odd world into which he'd reluctantly strayed, Umbulala grunted reassuringly under his breath, his embattled faith renewed for the moment. He slipped back several paces from the bamboo; then, seizing advantage of every shadow, slowly and silently oozed along the ground in the direction of the piglet. Creeping up behind a stand of buffalo grass he tucked himself up tight as a millipede.......and waited.

The unwary piglet moved closer. The distance between dropped away; when the moment was right the panther unfurled himself - and with comfortable ease, sprang like a coil released. It was over in a heartbeat. So quick, only as he stood ahold of his small quarry in the hushed moments following its dispatch did it dawn on Umbulala that here, clasped between his jaws, was no ordinary piglet. It was a harsh awakening because in a twinkling, in a rage of elephantine trumpeting and lion-like grunts responding to the distress squeals of its young, there came broiling from a thicket - like a blast from a blow-hole - the biggest, most belligerent pig Umbulala had ever set eyes on! Out of a rapidly unfolding horror that took him utterly by surprise, so fast was the beast travelling, loomed a boar of monstrous proportions covered all over in long, black bristly hair. Adding to this hirsute vision from the netherworld were gnarled, fungus-like swellings crusted like hoary battle-scars below a pair of smouldering eyes. With villainous intent, tusks glinting menacingly in the morning light, it had a fix on the panther, and no  intention of being diverted. The Giant forest hog had entered Umbulala's world.

The panther focused on the hog's face, or the frowning visage that passed for it - gruesomely contorted with malicious resolve, with eyes foaming at the corners completing a picture of demonic malevolence. The situation was rapidly becoming serious; the hog was making headlong for him, at speed. Umbulala was aghast, spitting and hissing in disbelief - this was no warthog blasting full pelt toward him! But too late the dawning. Caught off guard, the hog was all but upon him. In the beat of a bat's wing the big cat leapt upwards for his life into the air, only narrowly avoiding a broadside from the raging boar. Landing awkwardly, with the hog's tusks just scrapping his hind leg and ripping out some fur, Umbulala was left with little time to recover   -   the infuriated boar was turning in his own length and thundering back for a second attempt. Hastily flinging himself up onto his paws, the full unpleasantness of his predicament - complete and unabridged - hit Umbulala hard. Awkwardly crouched, with little room for manoeuvre, and a hog of monstrous proportions and volcanic bent bearing down on him, a breeze propitiously rustled by his ready ears:

"So you've met the Giant forest hog, never in the best of moods when leopard is around....."

it seemed to cruelly tease about his head,

"not least when the leopard has been so crass as to snatch one of its own! I fear you won't outrun this pig, so may I suggest turning your thoughts to flying?!"

And with that, his ears stretched taut to catch every life-saving signal and message going, there came a fortuitous flash of inspiration. With the operative notion 'flying' dictating action the instant the cat's wild-eyed gaze - desperately casting around for some way out - alighted on a branch slanting out above him, an idea for salvation took root. Jumping skyward with legs and forepaws at full stretch, still stubbornly clenching the piglet, the panther let forth a muffled, revelatory *yowl* in a flying leap that had to find its mark out of sheer necessity, or be doomed. The moment his paws touched wood his claws gripped ahold in the same breath - and he heaved himself up.

But all too soon it was clear something was terribly wrong. The branch was pliable and slithery - wrapped as it was in spongy moss all the way up. The panther's face registered consternation and bewilderment in mounting measure as he found himself sliding inexorably downwards. In spite of furiously digging his claws deeper in the bark, a slanting limb padded in moss and lichen makes for a slippery slope, however gentle the incline. In his haste the possibility of such a complication simply hadn't registered. The distance he'd covered through sheer momentum was now literally falling away. The big cat hoisted his back legs up under him in a frantic bid to halt his descent. But given his size, one undignified bundle continued to slip down the branch in a determinedly downward drop that abruptly petered to a halt when his startled rump connected with a crossways branch. Chance, fortune…….they assuredly favour the bold, however humbling the path or means of redemption.

Grateful, albeit shaken, Umbulala roused himself enough to make a valiant effort to snarl down at his antagonist - one irredeemably hostile, bellowing Giant forest hog undauntedly leaping up to get at the panther, its whole demeanour shouting it in one: split this currish cat asunder! The disquieting thing was the boar would have taken any opportunity to do just that - if serendipity hadn't secured Umbulala's deliverance courtesy of a simple, chance convergence of branches. With as much dignity as he could muster, the panther lifted his head. As he surveyed his situation a wisp of wind whipped past his head, stinging his snout and ears, still stretched flat against his head:

"You must get ahold of yourself if you're going to survive this venture...."

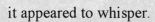

it appeared to whisper.

Startled out of a growing composure Umbulala let slip a back leg off the branch, managing only through sheer adroitness of mind, driven by survival, to swing it back almost in the same movment. Breathing in deeply, he took a firmer grip of his seat, propped centre of the union of the two branches where they ran together snug enough to hold him in place, spluttering unrestrainedly through clenched teeth:

"So this is the jungle being *with* me?!"

Still doggedly holding the limp body of the piglet in check with one paw, the panther turned to glance below. Able at last to observe this colossus of a hog somewhat less fraught of nerve and mind, he snapped querulously, wondering what could possibly possess nature to nurture a pig so big; a pig not only the size of a lion, but heavier! Worse, one with a decidedly unhealthy dislike of leopards. The boar eventually tired of trying to reach the panther, now well secured on a horizontal branch further up the tree. Yet notwithstanding the loss of the piglet, victory was clearly the hog's; if not exactly a pyrrhic victory of sorts, a moral victory at least. After all - he'd routed the mighty panther, letting all-comers know, first in a series of high barking *wah-wah-wah* calls to beckon kin, thence numerous grunts and growls to all and sundry. Swinging round, the huge beast lumbered over to his family, now fully emerged into the open from the thicket: a sow and three remaining piglets - nay hoglets - grunting and squealing in delight at the boar's performance. After much rubbing and snorting they went their way, the sow leading, followed by her young ones - with, bringing up the rear, the triumphant boar.

The panther coughed curtly into the breeze. He was well chastened. Short of it getting physical - *only* by dint of happenstance - he'd been given a sound drubbing. The Giant forest hog is a feisty adversary. Certainly one he wouldn't cross again in a hurry; with even young ones that are hardly piglets, but rightly *hoglets*. As such would he always defer to them. At that a breeze in seeming sympathy rustled softly through the leaves around him:

"Weellll...little brother, who'd have thought, yet another lesson all the way up here," it appeared to sigh in solicitous accord "where much that's odd slips the bounds of convention, slides just out of reach of understanding, where..."

before taking a seemingly stinging, albeit tongue-in-cheek turn,

"even the trees are slithery as mud....ahhh but wait, you know all about mud, you - and Sister catfish!"

The panther groaned to himself: Wind not only never forgets a transgression, but always manages to turn it into a lesson guaranteed never to be forgotten. The cat tried to relax, secure in the heart of the tree. He began to pick at his kill - but once reminded of the dratted catfish, another sorry saga of impetuous youth flooded back to him in torrents.

It had all transpired just after the rains. The dawn to dusk deluge that had flooded the low country was steadily receding in the increasing heat of the *dry*. Water that doesn't evaporate seeps underground, leaving behind muddy backwaters and pools that dot the slowly drying earth as a last reminder of the *wet's* benevolence. It's an interlude in the seasonal cycle that invites the watchful eye of the hunter more inclined to patient speculation, than hasty conjecture; the class of hunter, one doesn't doubt, the growing panther considered himself. Umbulala coiled his thick black tail round him and gnawed at a flea determinedly announcing itself under his fur. His vantage point from atop an anthill offered a fine view all-round.

With regulated humidity and temperature an ant-heap is a edificial triumph of compacted soil in which flying *white ants*, or termites, live in highly organised colonies in the stable atmosphere of a mound they develop over generations from a single, founder pair. From these venerable nests the termites plunder the immediate environs for decayed vegetal matter, bark and the like which they take back to their fungus gardens in the mound. Such giant structures - many termitariums can outlive the oldest elephant - are a honeycomb of storage cells, growth chambers, airshafts and passages to and from the outside that couldn't better demonstrate the ingenuity of the humble white ant. Moreover, with a hard outer crust, mature ant-heaps make pre-eminent lookouts of which the panther regularly took advantage.

The anthill sheltered in the deep shade of an Ebony tree, a fact adding significantly to its choice. Here he could lay back in reasonable anonymity and simultaneously attend to some vermin-busting. Launching an all over assault on general hygiene, licking his coat in no particular pattern, the mottled shade of the

tree flitted about the black leopard, chasing shivers of bronze across his hide one moment, gleaming blue-black the next. The panther was unashamedly proud of his glistening coat, so different from other leopards. In a leisurely mood he gazed out over the encircling bush. Sunlight danced across what remained of its once water-gorged traces. Scattered within easy distance were several small pools and puddles. One in particular drew his interest. It was just a tiny movement in the muddy water, a ripple. But this was a ripple with pep; with substance behind it. A small python maybe? Better still, a plump catfish....and at the very idea, thoughts salivating uncontrollably, his tongue whipped about his snout as if even his epicurean urges were daring him to go fish out the tasty morsel.

The lungfish - or catfish as its customarily known in these wilderness parts - is a remarkable work of nature. A carnivorous, aquatic leftover from primal times that feeds on other fish, frogs, worms, even baby birds, it can exist where water is only seasonal, surviving drought for long stretches by becoming dormant in mud. As the water in a pool or backwater recedes and dries up, a catfish will make a nest in the bottom of it. Rather like a cocoon, it seals it with a mud lid to leave only a tiny hole through which to breathe. Living on the fat in its body, the fish will happily hibernate in its 'dry sleep' until the rains again flood the area and liberate it. Other than bullfrogs, not many creatures are so favoured, and Umbulala mused on the wonder of it - able to sleep serenely in the bosom of Mother earth, while the rest of the jungle battles it out for survival in the heat.

With such an enviable advantage this particular catfish, as Umbulala smugly saw it at the time, might have been better advised to have buried itself deeper in the muddy remains of the pool as others of its kind had already done, instead of tempting fate by continuing to fill its greedy belly with the last of the pool's hors d'oeuvres. Acutely aware how his colouring put him at a disadvantage in open country he checked about him. Fine senses first scrutinized the near vicinity, thence the wider area with the consummate care of a future master hunter; a future master hunter for whom, in this instance, hasty conjecture was about to have the edge over old-fashioned nous. Once convinced all was clear, Umbulala leapt down from the anthill and bounded with uninhibited zeal toward the pool. Moving with all the impetuosity of youth, it was only when he went to check his pace that the rashness of his short, sharp dash dawned. Born of a mild excess of enthusiasm which normally wouldn't warrant a whisker raised, he was approaching the pool too fast. The panther let out an involuntary groan of self-reproach - error was jiving with him, a fact worsened by a brisk breeze, wheezing about his ears, seeming to whine: *too much haste little brother - Brother error will have his fun!*

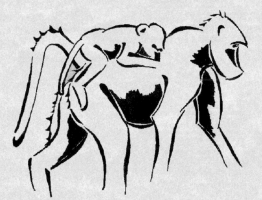

It wasn't the intrusive taunts of his own or others' making he needed now, but rather all his wits to muster the concentration that breeds inspiration. Contrary as it may seem, it was only while Umbulala was still in motion he had any chance of recovery - and in a flash, as he plummeted blindly toward the pool, a notion struck him. Knowing how they'd never failed him, the instant his paws touched ground he drove their hooked, curved claws in with rabid momentum. Thrusting them deep into the bed of the pool to anchor them in place, the hope was they'd work like cleavers to curb his onward rush and bring him to a halt.....and a reasonably dignified halt at that. But to his dismay it made no difference - the mortified panther proceeded on unchecked, sliding all the way into the heart of the pool where it was deepest, and muddiest.

Squelching and slipping through a quagmire whipped up into a maelstrom of red-brown mush, Umbulala was unable to slow his rate of acceleration, tumbling and turning and rolling this way and that in the morass before flopping to a standstill - sprawled on his belly, legs splayed akimbo. Pasted from head to tail-tip in a skin of sticky mud, ears plastered flat against his head, he blinked the sludge from his eyes as he worked himself up out of the slime, and onto his rump. The panther was not a happy sight. *An infant's error......and at my age,* his thoughts reeled in rhythm with the breeze whirling about him; the thought of a heckling Brother wind poking fun at him - not least agonized flashes of his lamentable open-air performance re-playing over and over in his head - only adding to his horror. There in the pool, basted from head to tail-tip in an unctuous glaze of slimy red mud, squatted one decidedly crestfallen panther.

But not for long. With a sudden movement between his front paws, the big cat rallied. A slim, fishy form was wiggling agitatedly; stringy fins, like long fleshy barbels or tentacles thick as an elephant-shrews tail, jiggled in the sludge. It was the catfish, cause of his public debasement: nay, the wilful unravelling of his reputation - *dénouement,* as the young panther saw it! Feverishly squirming in the mud in the hope of burying itself, it too had realised the error of its ways too late. But gluttony and procrastination, not youthful spirit, were this fish's downfall. Now, as watchful eyes were to record, one red cat was about to vent his frustration over a straightforward contest turned to fiasco for all to see. He slammed one mud-soaked paw down on his tormentor. But the slippery creature wriggled free. He next tried two paws, each with claws outstretched. But still the catfish eluded capture. Eventually, snout down and openmouthed, he plunged his questing set of fangs - glinting bright white in the sunlight, the only noticeable bit of him not yet coloured muddy brown - into the mire in final desperation.

With his tongue Umbulala could feel the catfish wriggling in the mud. Wrapping the fish in his mouth he gripped hold, and with unrestrained passion squeezed his teeth closed around it. But with decidedly little pleasure! The mud

was everywhere - down his throat, in his eyes....even his ears. Yet let go he couldn't; wouldn't. With the fish clenched in his jaws, securely pinned by canines clamped uncompromisingly in place, the panther stood up, mouth dripping mud. Shaking himself vigorously to clear every essential orifice of the all-pervading goo - not to mention every vestige of breath from the wretched catfish - the panther proceeded on with the arduous, humbling task of dragging himself free of the pool.

But humiliation hadn't yet finished with Umbulala. Every step forward was a step back as fat paws floundered and squelched about on the muddy bed trying to find purchase. Reaching the edge, it was only a short hop to the ant-heap - and sanctuary. But the ground between had been badly chomped about by the hooves of numerous ungulates using the pool as a surrogate oasis in the long dry. Subsequently it had grown into a stodgy wallow that stuck fast under foot. Not only that. Once Umbulala had freed himself of the pool, the clayey mud coating him had quickly begun to cake in the heat, until it was fast becoming akin to being encased in a membrane of quick-drying gum, heaping embarrassment upon discomfort in equal measure! There was only one thing for it - steeling every sinew to regain a semblance of dignity, Umbulala struck out in bold disregard, plodding stoutly - and increasingly stiffly - up to the anthill, head held defiantly aloft, his sorely-won trophy dangling with aplomb from his jaws.

Still humiliation hadn't finished with him. Little bigger than a guineafowl, one of the oddest looking birds to linger about water margins - where it builds nests capacious enough to take an ostrich - was flying lazily overhead on broad wings. The brown shape of a hamerkop stood out in the fierce blue of sky: a long, protruding beak on a large head made bigger by virtue of it having a permanent crest it can neither lower, nor raise. Calling out in a reedy song for all to hear, she flew low, lingering over the pool margins as though trying to identify the leopard:

"The jungle has a big *red* leopard; a big *red* leopard who eats fish! What will the storks and herons make of this then?"

Agonizing inwardly over the potential fun that was going to be had at his expense, Umbulala leapt into the air, neither appreciating the joke nor relishing the prospect, claws stretched to the hilt to silence the maddening hamerkop. Only because hamerkops are such master flyers did just a few tail feathers go astray as the claws found their mark. Her heart, nonetheless, was pounding as fast as her wings. She was out of her depth tangling with a leopard. Circling once more overhead the bird concluded it didn't much matter which leopard - a leopard it was, and she opted to beat a hasty retreat with a parting cry:

"The big *bold* red leopard won't forget this encounter!!"

No indeed. Umbulala shook his head, silently bemoaning what little hope there could ever be of him becoming a master hunter. Finding the deepest, darkest thicket to hide away his shame in - rather than prolonging the agony by returning to the anthill to exhibit himself further - he lay up in its shadow. Disconsolately cleaning himself of the mud, his spirits only lifted on thinking of the satisfaction he'd get eating the catfish. But even this small crumb of relief was short-lived. A rustle of wind through the branches above began to sigh about his head:

"Ahhh - life's little lessons again; there are as many lessons in life as shadows thrown by the leaves....." it appeared to whisper "even for master hunters. Once you stop seeking knowledge and truth Brothers' error and death are but a breath away. All are humbled by mistakes...."

Umbulala cringed as the wind seemed to whisper on unabated,

"yet male or female, the jungle over, master hunters only become master hunters because they *learn* from their mistakes."

Gazing down at the piglet, nay hoglet, Umbulala sighed resignedly at this last sober recollection of the catfish saga, knowing all too well the truth of it and the pain of it, and how nothing had changed.

As the memory of what wasn't one of his prouder moments continued to nag, he recalled how the catfish had suddenly begun to wriggle away. He'd stretched out a paw to restrain it, but the feeling of satisfaction he'd felt at the prospect of eating it had long fled. He had gone on to eat the fish of course. But then, as now with the hoglet, begrudgingly. And as the big cat returned to finishing off what remained of this latest, unsatisfactory catch, he brooded on how the past is never far behind - especially the very worst moments one would far rather forget.

Pangolin

MOUNTAINS THAT BRUSH THE MOON

A tree, from a seed no bigger than a grain,
outlives all life given breath the same moment

anguid pennons of hanging lichen, like so many fluffy manes and brush-tails trailing from the trees, lifted and swayed in the swell. A breeze wafted through the forest, setting to waltz along boughs furred in gilded moss, slithers of dawn light that little by little melted away in the crisp air into a filmy haze. It twirled up trunks and round branches, until tree blurred into tree in a softly rising mist that floated through the forest like a veiled, spirit of morn embracing all it passed, melding shape gently into shape.

Umbulala saw his chance: he slid down the tree, then slipped away through the gauzy paleness as unobtrusively as senses would allow. He simply couldn't countenance any creature beyond the Giant forest hog knowing what a fool he'd made of himself; add the uninvited recollections of the dreaded hamerkop *and* catfish and his discomfort was complete! And as he put more and more distance between himself and that unsettling haunt of the Forest hog, Umbulala concluded that the trouble with growing up is fate's cruel habit - for the sheer pain of it he didn't doubt - of recalling to memory past, often disparate events usually only related to the present experience by a single connecting factor: being unbearably uncomfortable as memories go.

Umbulala hadn't ventured so far up into the high country before; nor so deep into the rainforests. While much of what he was encountering was, if not new, plain weird, either way it held immense fascination for a cat, however much of the decidedly unnerving might be attached to most of it. Something of the latter was now infusing the panther's haste. In his desire to speedily remove himself to places more agreeable he'd - unconsciously and unwittingly - deviated slightly on his course. Instead of continuing up, he'd inadvertently headed off on a downward bearing toward lower latitudes. It was an accident of choice doubtless fired by an instinctive urge, common to all, to hightail it away from danger - or galvanising embarrassment, as here - along the easiest and quickest route out; and that's generally *down* and away rather than up and away.

Unfamiliar tracts full of the unexpected continued to yield up curiosities no inquiring mind could pass without stopping to observe. As now, with Umbulala. Never so intent on a course as to miss anything worthy of a second look, just one

glance of a Giant pangolin was enough to stop him in his tracks. Barely changed since time immemorial, the scaly ground anteater of forests and of woodlands is a quite extraordinary sight. Vaguely reptilian in cast, its humped, elongated body is covered over the whole expanse of its upperparts and underside of tail in rows of broad, overlapping scales formed of hair growing from its leathery skin. Worked by powerful muscles, they can be erected in defence, closed up tightly in an emergency, or simply flipped up to carry out some mundane, ever necessary domestic task, such as flicking out insects that fall into the crevices. With a cutting action that will sorely wound a snout or a paw, the scales overlap   - rather like that of certain tree cones before they release their seeds - to form a coat of horn-like plating that constitutes an unrivalled, protective carapace running all the way from forehead to tail-tip.

Despite a perversely small head and toothless muzzle it otherwise struck Umbulala as an immensely strong-looking animal, with stout recurved claws which, in addition to being clearly used for digging, probably also made formidable weapons. The cat was enthralled. As yet unaware of the panther, camouflaged in shadowy underbrush still veiled in the diaphanous half-light of daybreak, the pangolin was finishing off a feast of ants, trowelling them up with a wormlike tongue that's conveniently sticky with saliva for the purpose. To Umbulala, while it was obviously a ground-dweller, it was probably mostly nocturnal as it looked to move like an animal with poor sight - a lack nature usually makes up for with the other senses. Right on cue, as if to demonstrate it, the anteater winded the panther. Promptly shooting up onto its hind legs using its tail as a counter-balance, it lifted up its snout and, with eyes small and hooded, began to nod and prod about, sniffing and testing the air.

The Giant pangolin reserves a masterly trick for facing down a foe. True to its name *roller,* it will rapidly curl up into a ball; then, with its allover cuirass of outer scales rather like an impregnable shell, present a defensive shield more than adequate against most aggressors - a loud hiss and the renowned cutting ability of its scales being deterrent enough for the wise. And this was exactly what the pangolin now did…..........before executing one of the neatest escapes Umbulala had seen in a while. Taking advantage of the ground sloping away to a fast-flowing stream, the wily creature simply coiled up, then rolled downhill right into it! Bobbing up and down in the water, it floated downstream for a bit, then after what it obviously judged to be a sufficient safety margin, unfurled itself and swam off to the far bank where it clambered out.   As it melded into a tangle of shrubbery - doubtless off to sleep the day away in a self-dug burrow or abandoned aardvark hole somewhere - a bemused panther turned to continue on, wondering what further surprises Mother nature might have for him ahead.

The big cat didn't have long to wait. When a sharp barking hoot suddenly brought him up short, his first thought was baboon. But he fought shy of any certainty on that. The usual and the commonplace had been proving elusive. What would first seem familiar, would turn out not so; and too often to be accidental. If the grass, let alone the hogs hereabouts could get giant-sized, what else? He proceeded cautiously, nimbly scrambling up the nearest tree that looked to offer good coverage on an adequate enough perch from where to cast an unobtrusive eye about. But all around was heavy with growth, and the light poor. His view would have been all but limited to a short stretch up and down a game trail, if not for the fortuitous fact that his chosen vantage point abutted on an open patch of forest where one of the jungle's giants, a mighty tree once vast of crown, had crashed to the ground. Slicing through the treetops to open up a wide gash in the canopy, it had taken several others with it, laying flat a swathe of vegetation over a wide sweep. A simple act of nature that allowed the light to pour in to dispel the gloom and form a clearing, it was here he saw them.

They were a revelation. Not unlike baboons - but only fleetingly as there all comparison ended. Covered in long black hair and much bigger, their faces, too, were different; far more expressive in tone and wit. In fact more like monkeys than mean-eyed doglike baboons; and when standing upright on their hind legs they moved a little like hairless apes. The panther relaxed in his hide and watched wide-eyed, hoping to learn something of these curious beasts. He wasn't to be disappointed. All appeared to be adult. Two were larger than the rest, and if physical, almost aggressive body movements were anything to go by, most likely male; so furiously physical in fact, one appeared in the throes of a fit of rage. For the newcomer watching - one of the decidedly cool family felid

not given to brash, noisy behaviour - it was an unattractive performance little deserving of applause!

Vigorously, even hysterically rushing about, the ape was grabbing ahold of low-slung boughs, or any one of the plethora of vines looping snakelike in and out the trees like so many cobras. Frantically bouncing up and down on a branch here, shaking or jerkily swinging from a liana there, it finished off its frenetic display by jumping up in mid air and thumping the buttress root of a trunk with the flat of its feet. It did this again and again - in between much ground stamping and drumming of a log or surface root - accompanied by a gamut of facial contortions and verbalisations, from lip pursing, grins and grimaces to vociferous *hoo-hoo-hoo* calls in varied inflexions; with the pounding 'thud' at regular intervals of a hard-soled foot on wood reverberating above it all.

Umbulala intently noted every aspect of what he took to be some wild, display of dominance, and how the rest stayed well out of the way. His mind raced as to what they could be. As thought tumbled over thought the big cat suddenly let slip a gasped snort of surprise at what next caught his eye - these apes had no tails! Watching transfixed, it quickly became clear why: the prodigious strength of long, muscular arms - with which they were able to reach every part of their body and climb with ease - was such that there was no call for the additional use of a tail. Add a stout body and strong necks, and Umbulala concluded he might be best advised to avoid them altogether and seek out easier pickings; like the local blue duiker he'd heard made good eating.

Just then, as if struck by a small wind gust, the tree foliage shook, jerking the branch just enough to startle the engrossed panther:

"Wind - stop mucking around! It's essential I know what these monkey folk
are about!"

Obviously rattled, the big cat spat into the air, gripping the wood tensely with his
claws as if to steady himself.

"That's a band of chimpanzees - smallest of the great apes, along with their
more slender, more arboreal and amiable bonobo cousins....."

the mellifluous sound of something far less tiresome floated back from beyond a
cluster of leaves to the side of the big cat,

"who walk more upright, but prefer the deeper jungle tracts around the great
river many moons beyond these forests."

A dazzling sunbird astride a tree orchid, shimmering feathers reflecting brilliant
green in a shaft of sunlight piercing the foliage, sang out through sips of nectar.

A long curved bill, precisely and perfectly aligned for the purpose, was
elegantly dipping in and out a vivid spray of crimson and orange petals. Habitué
of the higher moorlands and heath forests where it prefers to nest and breed -
feeding on Giant Lobelias, tucking up in Groundsel ruffs at night, and weaving
nests from the woolly down of everlastings in the more sheltered tree heather -
this sunbird was clearly spreading its wings further afield to feed. Fixing his
gaze even more firmly on the chimps, Umbulala snorted, his eyes widening in
quiet disbelief:

"*Bigger* apes??? Little brother you jest!"

With a lightning flash of scarlet wing tufts hinting of its origins mid the higher
forests, the sunbird - a stunning Scarlet-tufted malachite - warbled back to an
alert panther:

"On the higher slopes they live, in and around the glades of herbs and great
moss-clad trees that roll on toward those misty places of strange, treelike
plants...." a glimmering green head nodded with growing enthusiasm "the
blossoms and ruffs of which we sunbirds are so fond. Believe me, hunter of

the night, their size in relation to these chimps is like that between a big lion and a small leopard."

Dismay and apprehension swept the panther's face in one, as in a low snipe of pique he chided himself for ever coming into jungle so thick one can bump into anything almost before scenting it, and where everything that's trouble - is huge! And as the cat moaned under his breath, a disquieting notion hit him:

"Brother sunbird - just what do these other giant apes eat?"

he hissed an urgent plea at the Malachite, a iridescent green shimmer now fluttering to another orchid.

"Oh they're not *meat-eaters*......." the sunbird trilled reassuringly "but forage on the celery, berries, bamboo shoots, nettles and the rest of the herbage that flourishs around that lush abode!" before delicately dipping a slender beak deep into the blossom's beckoning mouth.

A distinct look of relief crossed the big cat's pensive features, and he humphed begrudgingly. Yet sobering facts remained of which he was painfully mindful:

"Giant hogs, hairless apes, these chimpanzees...." the cat ruefully noted in solemn succession, "and now further up those slopes I've only had a rudimentary glimpse of even *bigger* apes - with me in the middle! Why, oh, why could Mother nature not have used Brother lion who's vain enough to look forward to such a prospect!"

Nothing could be more certain to soothe an increasingly raw-edged panther than the diverting notion of lion eagerly rushing to potential doom, and Umbulala composed himself accordingly. And, as if in empathy with his more sedate mood the soft cooing lilt of a dove - for Umbulala the very heartbeat of jungle and bush - floated up from an embrace of vegetation to kiss the air. Reconciled to a calmer self he settled back to ponder his situation. Serenity, however, was short-lived.

A loud ruckus exploded among the chimps as they burst, as one, into a wild, harum-scarum chorus of pant-hoots, chilling screams, and loud *WAA* barks and *WRAAAS* that cut to the bone. Umbulala's gaze flew to a sudden bustle of activity in the canopy above the chimps - and a striking sight appearing and re-appearing. Silky colobus monkeys, their white-mantled black coats distinctive mid the dense green of the foliage, were leaping from bough to bough, at times seeming almost to fly, the snowy-tufted tails of these gentle leafeaters swinging wildly. One suddenly separated from the rest high up a tree, the trunk of which a big chimp was simultaneously ascending, and very rapidly. Umbulala was astounded. Having taken them to be mostly ground-dwellers, he hadn't expected the apes to be able to climb with such speed and agility, assuming they were too heavy to climb that high and fast! Moreover, they were looking suspiciously like they had a penchant for meat. What, then, of the even bigger great apes?! More than a little disconcerted at what he was witnessing, there was less and less about these rainforest parts he was liking; not least certain of its inhabitants.

The fleeing colobus took a flying leap to an adjacent tree. Unfortunately another chimp was waiting, and just as the colobus went to grip a branch within reach in mid flight, it was jerked away, leaving the terrified monkey stranded in mid air. The colobus managed to grasp hold of a thick clump of foliage at its tip, but that was all. Not sufficiently strong enough to carry any weight, the wretched animal plummeted to the forest floor. With remarkable speed the chimp responsible hurtled down the trunk, scooped up the stunned monkey and scuttled up another tree, a flying phalanx of fellow chimps in hot pursuit, presumably with the aim of claiming a share of the spoils. Umbulala's gaze followed the big chimp, tightly clutching its catch by the neck. Now as he watched it dispatch the colobus - not in the clean way of leopard, but disembowelling it by tearing out a clutch of viscera, in this instance the liver, from the still living monkey - the cat recalled his first cubhood lesson about baboons, and how the big dogs will similarly kill duiker and impala foals. But where these large apes again part company with baboons is an alarming ability to work efficiently together, unhindered by much in the way of squabbling.

Using steady strategy and surprise, and not just rush and bluster, or force of numbers that typifies baboons, a couple of big male chimps will give chase - sometimes simultaneously above and on the ground - as others position themselves to block the victim's escape. It crossed the captivated cat's mind that, given the chance, an opportunistic band of chimps could well kill and eat a leopard! Almost at the moment of the kill, a frenzied bout of  celebratory screaming over and above the din of excited, hunting barks broke out among the chimps. Some of the bigger ones had by now scurried up the tree where the chimp with the dead colobus was cloistered; and while these crowded round among the branches for a share, others gathered at its base biding their moment to scale the trunk; failing that, the possibility of a tasty titbit, maybe even the whole carcass, dropping their way.

Most of the chimp youngsters had shown scant interest in the general mayhem, continuing to play some distance off. It was in this direction the panther's predatory eye now intuitively wandered, and zoomed in accordingly - on one young chimp in particular. It had a withered limb, and he wondered if it might be due to the virus that similarly afflicts hairless apes, paralysing their voluntary muscles to the point, so he'd heard, of immobilising limbs so completely the hairless ones can neither clamber about upright, sprint or climb. If indeed this was this chimps fate, it had got off lightly, frolicking and clambering about as reasonably as the rest. As Umbulala pondered this, another pair of pale yellow eyes was anonymously studying the distracted youngsters; eyes that from the adjoining banks of cover had also noted the youngster with the crippled arm. In leafy seclusion up his tree, the panther hadn't yet picked up on the presence of another major predator in the vicinity.

The young chimpanzees appeared to be playing a highly favoured game of chase: jumping and swinging in and out and between a fall of vines and lianas in a carefree spree of vitality and fun. It was at some point, unnoteworthy in hindsight, that the small chimp with the withered arm dallied a moment too long on the ground. It was a moment long enough. The undergrowth erupted in a blur of spotted leopard sweeping out, falling on the chimp in almost the same instant, and killing it with a single bite to the throat. The spotted cat didn't falter. In movements as smooth as liquid flows of sunlight, it had caught and carried its prize all the way up a tree it had doubtless earmarked prior to the attack. With a skin-smooth trunk free of any notches, shoots or minor branches for at least a giraffe's length from its base that might make for ready footholds, the tree also lacked any lianas, branches or vines that could link it with adjacent trees to form walkways and bridges. A perfect bastion in which to hold out against a throng of avenging chimps!

Confusion reigned among the troop. Satisfied feeding grunts briefly gave way to stunned silence, then as quickly again to a spine-chilling clamour of *wraas* and screams, as if each chimp was working its confreres up into a fury of bravado. Closing en masse on the tree concealing the spotted leopard, one of the bigger chimps rushed forward, slapping and stamping the ground and hooting loudly. Making as if to ascend the trunk the chimp instead leapt in the air, ready to drum its feet against the wood, when something soft and wet hit its shoulder. Startled off course, the big chimp dropped to the ground - and with it the eyes of every other chimp watching from behind dropped in unison.....only to fall on a darkening splodge on the rotting leaf cover under the tree where blood, in muffled rhythmic *plops*, was steadily soaking the padded earth. In frozen, transfixed silence the chimps slowly slid their collective gaze up the tree trunk, thence along a bough until it soon settled on a spotted, cold-eyed face in the foliage snarling back - and alongside, a small limp body. It was clear the leopardess could defend her position, inflicting grave injuries on any challenger that might try to come up after her. Of this there was little likelihood, given the impregnability of her stronghold. Realising it, the chimps began to depart one after another, their intention to forage, play - live another day - elsewhere.

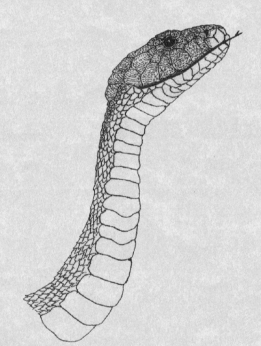

Umbulala had watched it all through eyes wide as guineafowl eggs. From start to finish he'd observed a master hunter at work. As smooth as a swallow in flight, the leopardess - for a female it was - had formulated a plan neat and slick as thought, and carried it off with a panache and vivacity that left him giddy. Selecting her victim and escape route she'd then, in accordance with these, executed attack and retreat taking full advantage of the entire adult chimps' distraction with the colobus. Without question here was a leopardess worth the reckoning; a mate worth crossing the rubicon for! He scrutinized from his high vantage point the ground below, the clearing and general environs so to plot out a route before breaking cover. Then, dropping straight out of the upper branches, he made for the tree harbouring the leopardess, an undisclosed zest infusing his every step. Yet he didn't rush. If she was the master hunter she'd shown herself to be, this leopardess would be in no hurry to leave her hold-out.

UMBULALA

Once at the bottom of it the panther stood a moment; then, slowly and deliberately he stretched his fine form up the trunk, reaching as far as he could with his front paws. Digging in his claws, he proceeded to rake them down the bark again and again. This Umbulala did with more than the usual enthusiasm, until the trunk bled with sap and he was sure enough certain he'd captured the attention of the spotted cat, now hurling spits of defiance down at him. Confident those blazing eyes would be following every scintilla of his every move, the panther fell back onto all fours. He turned; then with a flamboyant swagger performed at a infinitely studied pace - all the better for his handsome figure to catch the light - oozed into a slow motion strut of the coquettish, turn-a-head kind; the kind calculated to arouse desire, while showing off all his self-perceived magnificence to the full. Utilising every play of sunlight to utmost effect, the panther primped and preened and pranced about outrageously, gleaming alluringly in his shining black coat, and all for the benefit of his observer.

He next made great show of climbing an adjacent tree, ostentatiously scaling it with all the energetic dash he could muster – devil-may-carc verve and braggadocio in one - tempered with just enough nonchalance to make it appear that he always skimmed up tree trunks with such blinding physicality and vim! Umbulala insinuated himself along a branch roughly level to the spotted cat. Here he stretched out, a snaking, sensuous stretch, and began to lick himself. Fully aware how his plush black fur emphasized the healthy pink of his tongue, he did so over and over. He then yawned long and lazily by way of drawing attention to his fine collection of canines.......and as he did, he concluded he mustn't overdo it. By now she must be in no doubt - his unbridled ardour had been laid bare for all to see: here was one, big, willing leopard in his prime, and available. He at last made eye contact with the leopardess. She was as beautiful as she was bold, and to the panther's delight appeared to be appraising every facet of him - from tail to ear-tip.

Umbulala verily purred at her:

"It takes courage to take one from among a band of so many! Why, when there's plenty of easier prey?"

She blinked unabashed, and a soft, approving mewl floated lightly back through the hush:

"I hear there is only one leopard as black as night and large as a lioness. You must be Umbulala, who, as the jungle has it, is not without boldness. We all take easy pickings when chance offers - sometimes it's simple, sometimes fraught with danger; and, as you must concur....."

she turned her attention back to her kill,

"only the foolish starve to death among such bounty."

Then, almost in afterthought, she crooned beguilingly:

"I.....am Nyanga."

Umbulala was enchanted. Laying on the charm, he trilled by turn a response so enticing, only the hardest of hearts could resist its pull:

"*Nyanga*.....after Sister moon, with your golden head and sparkling eyes that dance like fireflies in the night. Ohhh, I see why *you* are Nyanga.....!"

And so the two leopards remained awhile in their respective trees, swinging between grooming and carolling to each other. Thus time passed. Then Nyanga, long finished her kill, began exchanging something of her jungle world with Umbulala.

She imparted much about the ways of the high country and of its creatures, all of it so very different to what was familiar to the panther - where even the stars and moon appeared too big for the heavens that held them. Here the stars veritably overflowed! Swirling in mesmerizing trails that swam all along the milky way and beyond, they were bigger, brighter and bolder than elsewhere;

while the moon, in its blue-black swathe of sky, was overwhelming. And as the black leopard reflected in quiet wonder, watching its huge, silvery face slowly sink behind the ice-capped crests of the peaks looming far away beyond the treeline, all at once he understood:

"*Now* I know why they are the Mountains of the Moon - it's as if those towering, white-headed peaks are drawing down the moon into the very heart of Mother earth."

Gorilla Knuckles

THIS UNSPOILED ARCADIA

When the earth speaks, hearts tremble

The view from where Umbulala and Nyanga lounged on their respective branches in a strapping forest tree was graced with a thrilling spectacle silhouetted against the sky - way beyond the heartland of the chimpanzees, the distant panorama of the snow-crowned, equatorial mountains. Often hidden in either a mass of cumulus cloud piled high, or haze, its picturesque sweep of jungle-choked slopes and white-glaciered peaks shone in the sunlight. They were the privileged recipients of a rare event: only fleeting breaks in the cover, or days uncommonly clear, will accord observers sight of the snowy summits of the fabled Mountains of the Moon in all their full, unrestricted splendour.

It was a magnificent morning, full of the promise of a new day, seemingly devoid of care. Indeed so free of care, a lighthearted Umbulala - legs dangling either side of the branch - began to harbour hopes of Brother wind having forgotten him; almost cherishing the notion as a reality, with the whole sorry saga then fading into obscurity. He'd never wanted to embark on what he considered a dubious exercise from the start anyway, snorting dismissively under his breath. Such thinking is understandable when one finds oneself alone, at the centre of a win-lose situation leaden with destiny. Life, after all, can be sweet: handsome company, a plenitude of food, a virtual cessation in the vexing constant of competitors - lions, wild dogs and the like - forever on the fringes or slavering at the feast; and sleep, rejuvenating sleep. Sheer bliss. And some challenges just aren't worth risking it all for.

The panther's relaxed eye strayed to a bird soaring high above the trees: an eagle languidly plying the air. The planform of a diademed crest - investing such a commanding cast - and broad rounded wings profiled against the sky makes the Crowned hawk-eagle instantly recognisable. To Umbulala all eagles without exception share the demeanour of a deity, of omniscient authority; and this majestical raptor was deserving of both title and rank. Powerfully built, among the strongest and biggest of the birds of prey in fact, Crowned hawk-eagles specialise in hunting monkeys and small antelope. Agile flyers despite their size, they can weave a flight path through a forest canopy with matchless skill. Dropping directly down from overhead straight onto a quarry, a supreme talent for weightlifting comes impressively into play as burly legs and formidable talons, together with the sheer, muscular strength of a hawk-eagle's wing power, enable it to seize, lift and take off vertically with its kill through the tree cover in one flowing movement. The panther was about to witness one such peerless display.

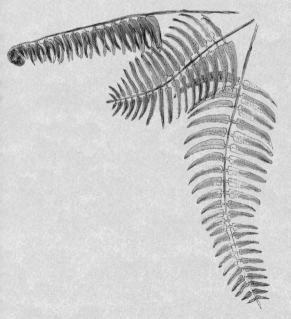

The hawk-eagle had floated in low over the trees, ominously circling by a waterfall slicing through the swell of green; a silvery sliver off which shimmers of sunlight sparked and glinted. In a movement slick as a flick of a bat's wing the big bird suddenly folded its wings, and with talons stretched to the full below it, dropped into the canopy like a rock. A flickering ripple of white dipping in and out the green betrayed a colobus leaping from tree to tree. Like the lightning-flash flit of a dragonfly over water, the hawk-eagle was on it, catching the monkey in mid air. In a single beat of mighty wings the eagle lifted above the treetops, and with its prey firmly in tow glided effortlessly away on the air currents, presumably off to favoured perch, or the more remote sanctuary of an eyrie set high somewhere on a cliff or mountain crag. The panther watched transfixed. The strategy, speed and agility of a bird as large as the Crowned hawk-eagle hypnotised his senses, and he enthused with all the admiration of one master hunter for another. Such power invested in a comparatively insubstantial form of flesh and feathers light enough, however big, to fly, is truly impressive.

He was reflecting on this amazing contradiction of factors cojoined in one bird when a hectic rustling suddenly started up in the foliage. With the gruff indifference reality keeps for moments of awed contemplation, the panther knew immediately. It had all been too good to be true. His harmless little fantasy, that Brother wind may have forgotten him, was just that - fantasy. And as he sighed resignedly, a sharp breeze whisked about the black shape stretched anonymously along the branch of the red-flowering forest giant; a handsome tree topped with a colourful crown dense enough to hide away in from anything - *anything save Brother wind* may well have been a rueful Umbulala's thinking at this juncture. With that there came a triumphant whine of breeze wheedling its way through the foliage:

"I've found the hairless apes! Below the nest of the hawk-eagle so beguiling you just now; beyond the last of the bamboo where the singing grass gives way to trees hung in lichen and ferns; thence on......"

it wheezed breathlessly on around the panther's decidedly unimpressed ears,

"through the tree heather to the place of the Giant Lobelias and Groundsel so favoured by Brother and Sister sunbird!"

If Umbulala was in any way feeling miffed about his hopes being dashed, this reminder of the sunbird assured he'd be even more so, and he gave vent to his displeasure accordingly. After all: did not that same bejelled denizen of the air declare that large apes don't eat meat? Yet within the flash of an elephant's ear did not he, Umbulala, witness apparently *lesser* great apes killing and eating a colobus? So why not the bigger ones, and through clenched teeth a sorely disgruntled panther hissed his dissatisfaction into the wind:

"And that's supposed to run me through with delight? I've just been given a repeat picture of where the sunbird claimed the *really* great apes live. Having witnessed the antics of the smaller ones, I'm now being presented with the unenviable ultimatum of enhancing my knowledge of the bigger variety by traipsing off to where *they* live! I'll probably end up smack in the middle only to be chastised with how, if I'd been wiser, I wouldn't have got myself mixed up with them!"

Umbulala was in no mood to bandy further, nor share his muddle of thought and feelings with Nyanga. He glanced across at her dozing, and with the merest hint of movement lest he startle her, slipped like molasses down the tree, thence off through a shadowy cover of green.

Yet Nyanga was far from asleep. In their brief time together the panther had hinted nothing of the daunting task that had brought him to her jungle world - a task dangerous, if not deadly - and the leopardess purred as she recalled how lighthearted he'd seemed, while knowing something of what Mother nature intended. It was now clear to her just how daunting a task, by the simple fact of the panther being called from so far away; and it set her to wondering, as Umbulala had, if there was no other who could take on such a mission?

"No....." she nodded to herself after only a moment's deliberation "it could only be one such as Umbulala."

She monitored his every movement as he melded away into the cover of jungle without even a backward glance; as if such a look might prevent him fulfilling his destiny.

Umbulala proceeded at a brisk pace. From the contrast of the jungle maze of the evergreen forest, with its richly varied web of plant and animal life, he entered the belt of the hollow-stemmed bamboo. This hushed haven of singular, towering canes, which generally rings the equatorial mountains in dense rambling stands, excludes virtually all other vegetation. It also invites only a select group of game, able to exist comfortably in it by virtue of keen smell and hearing and flexibility, foraging among its waving tops, or sheltering in its forest of poker-straight stems. The cushioning effect of the ground cover of ferns and moss, shed fronds and leaves under the big cat's paws was in perfect harmony with its muffled sound world, where even the canopy lets in only strained, suffused light. Some golden monkeys were feeding in the tops of the swaying bamboo stems, and Umbulala even thought he heard the whuffing grunt of buffalo off in a clearing somewhere deep in the bamboo. But that was all. Passing out of the last of its dimly lit traces, the big cat was almost relieved to find himself back in the rambling, forested meadows of the strange, moss-covered trees newly familiar to him from his demoralising clash with the Giant forest hog. Much more open than the bamboo, he nevertheless moved with care as with every pawfall, as the land sloped inexorably upwards, the going became increasingly interrupted by wispy stretches of patchy mist.

As on all the great equatorial mountains one climbs through a swathe of mixed evergreen forest en route to a bamboo belt of varying density; sometimes beyond the bamboo too. As now, before the tree heath winds on its upward ascent to the rarefied otherworld of the alpine moorlands of the higher reaches. Dotted with the occasional stunted clump of bamboo the scene that rolled before him wove a picture of an elysium unchanged for moons too many to grasp, as if nature had fallen into a dreamy half-slumber in long-fled memory, and never fully awoken. Dominating lush, grassy glades of herbs and wildflowers were the same haunting trees draped in trailing lichen, vines and narrowleaf ferns, limbs thickly cushioned in moss he might only have recalled snatched glimpses of, yet the feel and texture of it was etched in memory; trees, huge of trunk, their branches running almost along the ground before veering skyward; others, tall

...l berries; with scattered through it the

...verlastings and the rest, weaving it all

...leasured the eye.

...d in moss and lichen, and in places the

...nd leaves, the panther needed his

...Given his last experience in similar

...with Brother forest hog - he was at

...d scent of the area, and remembered

...red the purlieus of the great mountain

...o herbage, looked as if it never wanted

...rich, even the trees had turned their

...ens of fungi, blossoms and feathery

...of haze, a haunting quiet pervaded the

...hirrup of a bird that seemed to choke

...d, not even of cicada. Indeed animals

...hose he did catch a glimpse of tripped

...mbulala wound his way to a rock ledge

...climbed up, slipping a little on its skin

...atch he squatted as comfortably as he

...ear, sunny gully that broke like a gash

...'s large ebony head lifted to sniff the

...ent new to him. As an overwhelming

...ously: *Giant ape?!*

...ncentrate his attention, something real

...e spot. A movement ahead held his

gaze, and Umbulala focused in. There was one at first; then another; then several. His jaw dropped - and with a sudden sinking feeling a gentle breeze ventured what he suspected but, going by what his eyes were revealing, would prefer not to believe:

"At last, Umbulala....." sighed the wind, "the giant apes; the big one out front of the others is the leader. Splendid, don't you think?"

Here before the panther were the magnificent Mountain gorillas of the upper forests, feeding serenely in a sun-splattered glade overflowing with a fecundity of plant life. Umbulala gulped as he took in the huge black forms, greater in size and shape than any hairless ape he'd seen, their thick fur aglow with health. The lustrous coat of the imposing one turned away from him looked as if it might even have been brushed across its back with powdery moondust - perhaps only too aptly, here in this unspoiled, bowery arcadia, gazed on as it was from afar by the silvery peaks of the Mountains of the Moon.

Surrounded by such superadundance, no gorilla hurried as it fed, nor jostled for some plum piece of herbage. There was an obvious enjoyment in the feeding process none appeared to want to race. Each morsel was savoured, every stage - from picking, to popping in the mouth, to eating - undertaken with relish. With such a fertile cornucopia of fodder around them, the group, adults, adolescents and babies alike, all aimlessly foraged about in a sort of organised disorder; there was none of the hectic hijinks of the chimps he'd just encountered, nor the fractious rush of baboons. While most ambled about feeding - a palmful of berries here, a clutch of nettles or a chewy chunk of bark or fungus there - one adult dozed in the moss-padded fork of a tree; another lolled luxuriantly on a patch of flattened greenery as it basked in the sun, one leg crossed over the other; while elsewhere, balanced on its mother's head, a chubby moon-eyed baby agrip a trailing creeper nibbled a tree orchid as, unfazed, its patient parent nonchalantly peeled a celery stalk.

Despite the tranquillity of the scene before him - punctuated with an all-round soundtrack of snapping vegetation, belly rumbles, grunts and belches of contentment - the panther, a giant of his own kind, inwardly quaked:

"These apes have to be seen to be believed!"

Indeed. The huge domed head of the Mountain gorilla silverback is enough.

"As for the thick neck....." Umbulala brooded soberly, "only an exceptional leopard, if so inclined, could bite through that; while with those shoulders and limbs..." he observed more ominously, "one could snap a cat not on its mettle in half!"

From Umbulala's viewpoint the sunbird was certainly right on one point - they're bigger than lions. Just then another silverback, virtually the same size, hoved into view a little way beyond the rest. Guessing it to be younger by its more hesitant gait and movements, Umbulala hissed under his breath:

"A would-be leader - as long as it keeps enough space between itself and the older silverback, still in its prime and not looking to be reckoned with rashly!"

A breeze began to play lightly, if not a little mockingly about the panther's head:

"Ohhhh mighty cat of the night! Master hunter you most certainly are as you've sized it up perfectly, and....."

it appeared to whine on in outrageously

fawning approval,

"missed nothing in your assessment!"

Such spontaneous praise from Wind was more than unexpected, it was deeply suspicious, and the panther spat into the breeze:

"If Mother nature thinks for one instant I am going to tangle with these brutes" he seethed "then you've *both* developed the brains of Go-away birds! This is enough. I'm off!"

A previously calm breeze whirled into a sudden gust, a veritable mini vortex of wind, that whipped frenziedly around Umbulala as he rose up on all fours:

"Little brother........",

it coaxed past ears professedly deaf to outside influence, pasted flat as they were against a decidedly peevish panther's head,

"mighty cat of the dark....."

it appeared to sigh,

"you take me wrong; perhaps I *have* failed to enlighten you fully on the task ahead!"

Umbulala had the satisfying feeling that at last, if only figuratively, he had Brother wind like the gullet of one of his victims - between two hard places, his top molar and his bottom molar, and squeeze he would. The cat let out a dismissive snipe:

"Be off with you Brother wind as *whatever* that task is it's liable to get me injured - a little like the dampness of this place, it reeks a bit!"

Suddenly the whole tone of the moment altered; gone was the waggish ambience hitherto infusing it as the wind promptly began to blow with a dramatic urgency, almost suppliant in its intensity:

"Umbulala - it's not the gorillas you're here to confront,"

it seemed to sigh and implore,

"Mother nature is trying to save the jungle!"

Umbulala turned to flounce off, snapping back:

"Noble sentiments like that aren't going to stop me leaving."

Almost in the same instance the panther's reaction brought a frantic response from the wind. With stinging force it whooshed back ever more frenziedly - seemingly ever more desperate to hold his attention:

"You're here to save *gorillas*!"

The panther froze in his tracks, not quiet believing what he thought he heard on the wind. In no mood to appreciate the difference, his thoughts screamed in silent indignation as he sputtered into the breeze in cold, livid defiance:

"Save these great brutes, liable as they are to have little care for the likes of me, a leopard, more probably considered a foe of the gorilla than a friend? Had I known this was what I was called here for I'd never have come! Away with you Brother wind.....and shame on Mother nature for this arrant duplicity. I'll have nothing more to do with your conniving plans!"

The wind, previously blowing a near tempest around the big cat, dropped to an ingratiating whisper of a breeze, just soft enough to be noticed:

"I will tell Mother nature as you wish....."

it appeared to caress obsequiously; then with a certain acerbity,

"but she and Mother earth may have more to say about this shameless rebellion!"

Honouring the message on the wind with nothing less than a vituperative snarl, Umbulala snapped at the air. It all rather rankled, and flinging himself off the ledge, he swung away down a long slope into an inviting clearing awash in sunshine. As in the gully, the mist had lifted here too. In one fluid movement - a mix of sensual abandon and exasperation - the panther slung himself into the seductive patch of sun, defying even his own thoughts to show him if there *ever* was an animal that had helped another of a different kind. Unless to get something out of it of course: like ox-peckers, plovers, egrets and their ilk with buffalo, hippo, crocodiles and others; relationships as self-serving for the birds as for their hosts, offering easy pickings in a plethora of insects and parasites on the hides, even the teeth of animals more than willing to be relieved of them.

It all seemed too ridiculous to contemplate, and shaking his head as if to affirm his disbelief, the big cat concluded there could be only one explanation. Brother wind had been up in the high country too long and the damp must have got to some vital functions; coughing contemptuously about how even ox-peckers have their limit! With this the matter was perfunctorily dismissed, and the big cat began to doze fitfully in the warming beat of the sun. It soothed and calmed him; and as he dreamily began to see-saw between sleep and waking, long-buried memories started to meander sneakily to mind as, unsolicited, Umbulala began to indulge in reminiscences he generally wouldn't have bothered to recall; recollections triggered - rather more by design than accident - by his chance musings on the ox-pecker.

Relaxing more and more into the soporific caress of the sun, he began to picture himself lounging in an old Fever tree - a particular favourite as a lookout-cum-larder - with a half-consumed bushbuck carcass stashed in a fork above him. He was but a little way up from a river with a view over both banks. In his mind's eye there was nothing unusual about the scene or the setting - an amicable enough one of reeds, waterlilies and the usual preponderance of life coming and going. Then, little by little, the cat's thoughts began to wander on again, to sift relentlessly back over his life - all the way to early cubhood and a day at another river's edge when recklessness nearly cost him his life. It was the occasion of his first foray after bullfrogs and one which had met with blatant failure for all to see. Umbulala squirmed. The

shame of it was still real; even worse was the day-dreaming and loss of concentration, root cause of his hunting fiasco, that had next led him - all the teachings of his mother tossed aside like overworked scraps - headlong into danger.

Stretched out in the clearing, still enfolded in an embrace of sunshine, the big cat groaned inwardly; and as he did it seemed to spark a hunch, like an ember tossed into his drowsy thought processes, that all this recalling an experience not worth the pain of it had to be leading somewhere. Indeed it was. That fateful day, forever etched in unforgiving memory, was when the chameleon saved the cub Umbulala from a dread end in the jaws of a crocodile. It was also the panther's first experience of an animal helping another! Suddenly the irony of remembering it at this juncture struck him hard through his sun-drunk torpor; an irony given added trenchancy by the fact he was finding it impossible - in the distorting haze between sleep and wakefulness when the head can be a storm of mental ferment attached to a body desirous of nothing but slumber - to shake off his wonder at the kindness one jungle creature could show another.

Even at such a young age the panther wouldn't have hesitated to attack and eat the chameleon if it had been nearer. And as this niggled him, napping still in his sunny snuggery of solitude, a breeze wafting by seemed to whisper through his sleepy daze: *then, as now, Umbulala: Mother nature smiles on you.* Dreamy reminiscence wandered back to the Fever tree, then on again; this time to an episode far later in the panther's life in a similar setting. The adult Umbulala was again lolling in a tree overlooking a river; but now the bushbuck carcass was gone and the lovely yellow-barked tree - so called because of a fabled, yet erroneous link with the fever mosquito - had transmogrified into an equally fine Pod Mahogany of generous spread.

Again in imagination there was nothing untoward about the scene slowly unrolling. Game trails, pockmarked with the spoor of many, wound down the banks. In a veritable *tableau vivant* of pastel abundance, waterlilies bobbed on every ripple as cormorants, wagtails, kingfishers and an array of waterfowl fished and dived and swooped about. One present in ample number was the jacana or lily-trotter, the jungle's pet name for these jaunty birds, so called after the knack they have for tripping across lily-pads, elongated toes and splayed feet allowing them to walk on floating vegetation. Always smartly turned out in a chic ensemble of chestnut, gold and white, neat heads capped in glossy black, they're a distinct part of any river habitat where waterlilies thrive, feeding on every insect going, from larvae up.

To the back of this pleasure ground of activity and colour a hippopotamus was furiously twirling its tail - a habit with the matchless effect of spraying the dung everywhere. One of the many jungle fables of his mother Ingwe was the tale she had for why hippos indulged in what, to a cat, was one desperately, untidy sanitary activity! When the jungle was created, so it went, hippopotamus were given the task of keeping the grass trimmed for others. But hippo suffer sorely from too much sun, their hides blistering and cracking if exposed too long. So entreaties were made to Mother nature for them to spend the day wallowing in pools and rivers so to keep their leathery skins cool and moist, and leave the cutting of the grass to night. Mother nature feared they might consume all the fish. But assurances were given they wouldn't. And so has it long remained: hippos spread their droppings for all to see they've kept to their bargain with nature.

Umbulala mentally stepped back and began to visualize the picture in full panorama, complete with sound effects - hippos snorting water and *muh-muh-muh*-ing as they dotted the water like well-endowed islands replete with hidebound feasts: grubs for the escorts of small fish, and blood-sucking flies, ticks and the like for their back-perching birds. Prime among these fellow travellers of the ox-pecker, were numerous crisp, white egrets, always among the most dedicated of participants. A small herd of slender nyala entered the panther's field of view, a few adolescent calves at heel. Their appearance at the top of the bank, in concert with the simultaneous arrival of some noisy francolins and a flight of equally vocal Egyptian geese, was clearly too much for a lone, spiral-horned kudu who skittishly hastened off in protest. Mustering in a clutch of white-stripes and coppery splendour, ears and noses primed to detect anything untoward, the herd descended en masse to the water's edge. As one shiny-coated nyala after another took its fill, there was nothing overtly noteworthy about it all. Certainly nothing to warrant Umbulala recalling it as, once refreshed, each took it in turn - out of habit, but an intelligent rule of caution nonetheless - to ritually check the general environs and route back up the bank. Nothing, that is, if not for what was about to unfold.

With the attention of most now drawn away from the river, the shallows behind them erupted, startling even Umbulala in the tree. With scabrous jaws stretched wide, a crocodile burst like a bolt out of the churning torrent of froth and spray, to catch an nyala by the leg. An unattractive end for yet another thirsty antelope, might have been the conclusion of any observer. Not so. The panther could barely believe what followed. From out of the adjacent shallows hurtled a hippo angled on a headlong course for the crocodile. Shocked instantly into evasive action, the big reptile dropped the buck: a full-grown hippo bearing down on it - cavernous mouth brandishing long tushes, primed and formidable - being incentive enough for any creature to cut and run! Using its powerful tail as support, the crocodile swung round on its hindlegs, and in a green-brown blur swept back into the river, put to flight for all to see. There was little likelihood of the intimidated saurian salvaging any dignity either; not when its submerged retreat could be plotted all the way by a tell-tale trail of lily-pads showily nodding in its wake as the scaly body brushed against their long root systems - giving rise to bumpy work for the jacanas, and much mirth in a certain tree.

In the natural world of the jungle an ungainly hippopotamus storming to the defence of an antelope seems unlikely enough. What now transpired would astonish even the most hardened. It left Umbulala moonstruck. The hippo crashed to a halt at the water's edge. Once assured the crocodile was gone she turned, and trundling over to the stunned nyala, shovelled it up in her great jaws. She then waddled three or four buffalo lengths up the bank cradling the doe, all the while moving with noticeable care, doubtless not to jolt or alarm the doe further. Placing the nyala down on a soft bed of grass the hippo squatted, and

with her gargantuan mouth stretched wide open, like a giant mussel, proceeded to shade the animal from the hot sun. Against all odds, and every convention, the nyala began to rally. She got to her feet; then on unsteady legs began to gingerly pick her way up the embankment to the waiting herd, as much stunned into rapt stillness as the panther in the tree and, no doubt, a waterbuck doe calmly peering out over her shoulder from a thorn thicket; in the way of her kind, eminently alert and serene all in one.

Regaining her feet the hippo stood awhile watching the doe. Then nonchalant as you like she trotted back down the bank, just a hint of a swagger in her step; back to her preferred domain, as if saving antelopes from crocodiles was all par for the course. What was so lastingly memorable about it all for Umbulala - so dazzling, moons seemed to fly by, yet it had transpired over the briefest of interludes - was how a lumbering hippo had galumphed in to defend a nimble-footed, landloving antelope; two, very different paths that rarely cross. And here lies the heart and soul of it. Try as one may to put motive down in such situations to basic self-interest - competition for food, space, avenging the death of a calf or mate, group protection, genetic continuance, territorial dominance - rather than to altruism at its purest, doesn't always fit. Umbulala sighed: the wisdom of nature never ceased to fascinate him.

Could it really be, he wondered in his half-daze, that some animals come to the aid of others for no other incentive but to help? Without any prospect of gain not outwardly evident; for what is best perhaps described in the language of the jungle as a perk, a fringe benefit? As is commonly found with advantages indirectly derived from the actions of others. Examples of this are legion: the keeping open of rivers by the movement of particular animals along them; by what they eat of water plants which would otherwise overgrow and clog the channels; the keeping in trim of vegetation by certain species that, if not checked, would drain the water-table or strangle the plants others eat; pests that would overrun an environment to the detriment of all if not preyed on by the few; those who pass in their droppings remnants of indigestible plants now made edible for others; even seeds which won't germinate until they've passed through the gut of particular creatures. It seemed to the panther that any arguable benefits hippos might derive from what antelopes deposit in a river, have to be weighed against the more direct relationship hippos have with crocodiles.

As he understood it, their coexistence in river systems is a vital ingredient in retaining the health of them. Hippos assist the uninterrupted flow of a watercourse. By their sheer bulk they keep open passageways through floating vegetation which, if allowed to run rampant, will choke river channels; their movements stir river bottoms, releasing nutrients that favour certain river life; their excrement fertilizes and encourages algae to flourish, benefiting fish that eat other vegetal growth and any associated insect irritants that result. In turn, the crocodile helps maintain a profoundly crucial species balance among the fish population by culling carnivorous varieties to limits that don't threaten annihilation of the other species, without which the algae, the water vegetation, insect population, and so on, wouldn't be kept in check, and would thus otherwise expand to negative levels detrimental all round.

Looking back through his dreamlike fog it was an amazement undimmed down all the moons since it had been played out before him; an amazement nearly matched by his present befuddled state. There in the clearing where he still lazed, it was as if he was being held in suspended animation for the deliberate purpose of recalling the event with the hippo and nyala; as if it had some precise resonance for the present. And with that, a dawning awareness began to surface steadily through the daze! Umbulala shook himself from his sun-bedazzled whimsy, thoughts screaming:

"I know what's happening - they're trying to get round me. Well....."
he hissed, unmoved,

"it'll take more to win Umbulala over. Why, between Wind and Mother nature a cat could get killed!"

The panther had barely given vent to his frustration when the ground under him grumbled and trembled with such a force, it shook the trees around the clearing. Brought stingingly back to reality, Umbulala sprang onto all four paws just as another tremor struck - this time with a violence that not only vibrated through every rock and stone, it threw him across the ground. Up onto all fours again, he steadied himself, casting furtive glances about as if searching for an explanation. Noting a game trail that headed away through the surrounding tree cover up a long slope, Umbulala dashed

along it fast as his thundering heart and flying paws would take him, on up to a high promontory. From here there opened out a sweeping view across the jungle canopy. It ranged far and wide - with, in distant backdrop, a pair of peaks that were the very heart and soul of it. One slightly to the side behind the other, they were also the core of the frightful force now shaking the earth apart.

Impala

RIVERS OF FIRE AND BLOOD

Woe to those who break the web of life

hat greeted Umbulala's startled eyes was barely describable. Clouds billowed from the furthermost summit. Elsewhere, in an atmosphere of ash and smoke that all but blanketed out the light in parts, wisps of steam sighed and belched from jagged cracks in the tree-studded slopes, while from holes in ravines and gorges, spurts of red liquid squirted. The panther rushed to the edge of his rocky observatory where it looked away to the far side of the twin peaks, then on beyond to a distant body of water. Here, also, clouds were rising. Reminiscent of the great columns of flies that hover in large congregations over some of the equatorial lakes, these, however, weren't sooty black. They were white and aery, hovering like dragonflies' wings over a sun-dappled lake shimmering silver-gold in the surrounding green of jungle.

The uppermost flanks of the lakeside slope of the mountain were twisted and contorted. Where a ridge had split open, fiery, bubbling trails were squirming out from explosion vents like intestines from the bowels of the volcano; as if indeed the belly of Mother earth had been ripped asunder. They joined in a spitting stream to spew down the mountain and dissipate in the lake shining in the distance where, with the sudden onrush of heat into the water, steam had quickly begun to rise to form the white, vapoury clouds floating over it. With a constant moaning sound, like the groan of a beast of nightmare murmuring away in the dark, the river of liquefied rock broiled down the slopes. This was no river in the life-enhancing sense. It was a prowling track of blood-red, molten earth, seething and spluttering and streaked with bands of ash, with uprooted trees and bushes, boulders, rocks and anything else free-standing, all floundering in its wake.

Watching at a distance from his hillside promontory Umbulala, like surely every other creature on the periphery, was struck nearly senseless by this monstrous spectacle - or what perhaps is a truer depiction: this spectacular affirmation of the monstrous power of nature. Modest as it was on the scale of volcanic eruptions, it was still impressive; when not expected, terrifying. Not the best of moments then - given there wasn't much in the way of humour abroad in the air - for the wind to blow a gale about the panther's ears, whistling a message intended, in that loneliest of perches above the jungle, only for the panther. It was a message ripe with meaning, and no better moment to deliver:

"The Volcano speaks, Umbulala…..."

so a breezy whisper seemed to bounce off the sheltering rock around him,

"for Mothers' nature and earth. They are not happy; so much so earth has vowed to take you in hand if Mother nature won't. And as is being ably demonstrated, there's little doubt the will is there. They still smile on you, for this is but a modest taster. For how much longer, depends on you."

Umbulala was contrite.

"Is this what's called gentle persuasion?!"

one very subdued cat groaned back. But he had no fight left; not against the might of nature and the will of the earth:

"Soooo….." he sighed resignedly, "let it be….", and in that instance the earth ceased its trembling, as if holding its breath in anticipation.

"Hairless apes have come to kill gorillas….."

the wind appeared to sigh in ominous disapproval in and out the stony clefts,

"and smuggle their young from the jungle. Your mission is to halt them. Nothing can be allowed to die out without thought as to what may replace it; nothing is valueless in nature. That you've been set a formidable task....."
the breeze welled up with chilling resolve, stinging the panthers ears with intent,

"there's no doubt. But such displays by Mother earth are rare, so it cannot be stressed too much just how imperative it is you succeed. At first light make for those moss-ridden tracts of meadows lush with herbage below the Hawk-eagle's eyrie - there I will advise you, cat of the night."

Umbulala remained where he was, very still, and very thoughtful. He was in no hurry; rather, as he appraised it from the luxury of distance, in absolute awe of the devastation beyond. All plant life in the path of the heaving, fuming onslaught of lava had been swept away; just the charred vestiges of a few trees standing gaunt in the scorched destruction. With dusk, thence night descending, an ethereal patina fell over the scene, declaring it time to shroud the jungle's wounds from view. First an orange-red glow suffused the distant peaks. It rose in radiance, seeping into the deepening blue - a wave of spectral colour, flushing to crimson awash with violet, that swelled up and out across the darkening sky as if, as Umbulala saw it, myriad purple-breasted sunbirds amassing together were taking to wing all at once.

The air grew crisp and cold and an icy breeze played about his whiskers, nipping at his snout and eyes. But Umbulala was determined to watch on. The jungle of his experience didn't often speak in this way, and he felt compelled to take in every moment of the dying embers of what had transpired, as if indelibly recording its passing in his mind's eye. The big cat gazed on spellbound. With sharpened senses exhilarated as never before in the presence of such an earth-force, never had the possibility of his own existence being of little significance before the unpredictable might of nature struck him so powerfully. While the breeze whined and moaned in and out the cracks and hollows of the rock around him, a silvery moon rose to shed its dusty light. Lava flows, cracks and explosion vents were weaving a flickering mosaic in the dark, beading and spiralling round the slopes like the flight-trails of so many fireflies. As the moon floated nearer, the outline of a towering shape, another just beyond it, grew increasingly distinct soaring up into the extravaganza of stars - unchanged beyond the reach of memory - that stretched away to infinity. So it remained until dawn began to stretch its tentacles round the sky.

Beneath an azure horizon smeared crimson and gold from end to end, sunrise washed gently over the jungle. As daybreak ushered in another mother-of-pearl morning, a spreading shadow enveloped the canopy. Beyond it smoke and steam still wafted from the volcano slopes. Umbulala, however, was set to travel in the opposite direction; away from the smoking, smouldering earth. Dropping down the slope from the rocky parapet that had privileged him shelter - and a perspective on a pyrotechnic wonder he'd recall the rest of his days - the way became increasingly slippery, with cooling patches of mist coming and going at the whim of the sunlight. The drizzling precipitation of early morning drenched his coat, eyes and paws; only a powdering of ash over the dank vegetation - silent fallout, like some sombre postscript to a cataclysm - hinting of earth's fiery storm in the peaks far beyond.

Now and again Umbulala would stop, shaking himself vigorously to rid his coat of dew. It was on one such halt his nostrils were assailed suddenly by a putrid smell wafting his way on a breeze. It emanated from a density of shrubbery and trees up front of him…..and stank of death. With there being no scavengers to speak of in the high forests what dies, rots - accompanied by every unimaginable odour going. All at once an ear-piercing scream sliced the dewy air - *caution hunter of the night!* The sheer abruptness of it smote Umbulala's senses like white heat through ice; his blood ran cold, and for one, brief, heart-stopping instant, his head even seemed to drain of all thought. A tree hyrax was wailing a high-pitched warning down to a panther too frozen-jawed to respond: *hairless apes are about, and Brother death has danced a shameful dance.*

Alert as he already was to the presence of something decidedly unsavoury, the chill shock of that cry still ran Umbulala through. Assuredly among one of the more unnerving sounds the jungle can conjure up - most particularly when not anticipated - it so rattled his equilibrium he wouldn't be surprised to be deaf to his own pawfall! The panther gave his head a fierce shake to knock some serenity back into its thought processes; then with a grateful nod up at the tree canopy for a warning from a jungle compatriot he hadn't even laid eyes on, continued on through the dank cover of greenery, ever more stealthy of step. The denseness of the vegetation began to thin, taking on a more varied blend. Before long it opened out onto a vista of a wide mix of flora bathed in the softer sunshine of the high mountains, its veiled opalescence far removed from the searingly bright light of the low country.

Something immediately aroused his curiosity, not out of any unbridled admiration nor, as he'd noted already, the peculiar beauty of many of the trees and plants of these parts. A fair portion of the vegetation before him appeared wind-blown and scruffy; indeed tatty, as if it had been severely shaken and tossed about when the earth shook. Stepping around a frenzy of torn and ripped greenery strewn over the ground, the panther soon realised it was the work of a feeding animal, rather than a result of the violent upheaval in the volcanoes across the way. And a profligate one at that too, in his estimation!

Much of the foliage, flowers, fruit and herbs - even bark - snapped off or broken open had been only partially eaten. No sooner did he begin to nose around when he picked up the scent he'd encountered in the gully. With a dismissive sniff, the cat glanced about at the discarded vegetation he took to be the 'leftovers' of foraging gorillas. As for what they get up to close-up, this was the first chance he'd had for a snoop round on the quiet, and he wasn't impressed:

"What a waste, just like the elephants; worse - those maddening monkeys with their fruit!"

Turning disdainfully away Umbulala moved on, angling his pace into the wind. A light mist began to close in. As it did, a breeze cut back over his ears in sharp reminder of how these 'leftovers', he so underrated, provide vital sustenance for a plethora of ground-dwellers unable to forage on what they can't reach. It's an age-old process which, together with animal droppings and the rest, disintegrates into nutrients to nourish the soil; with even ants taking a share underground to feed the earth and its plants in return. *Nothing is wasted,* the breeze seemed to whine about his head, before abruptly trailing off as a grimacing panther suddenly stopped dead in his tracks. It happened in a heartbeat. As an overwhelming stench hit him full in the face the mist lifted, and Umbulala glimpsed a shadowy, black form up ahead, slouched under a tree.

Slick as thought the cat dropped onto his belly, his upper lip curled back, and slithered forward, the ground's dank padding of leaves muffling any trace of sound. With the foul fetor intensifying with every smidgeon of space he snaked closer, there loomed full into view a huge, lifeless figure. It was slumped at the base of a mighty, fern-clad tree, with draping vines and moss-clad limbs flaring sideways and up from its massive trunk; a charismatic tree with an aura and look once seen, never forgotten. As visions of slippery branches and Giant hogs flashed to mind, threatening to waylay Umbulala's concentration by whisking his thoughts off in disconnected directions, the wind whistled divertingly by, appearing to sigh:

"Well done, hunter of the night: you've found it!"

Umbulala spat into the gust whishing about him:

"What horror am I being led to? My every *sinew* is tense with rebellion; every bone chilled with apprehension."

Flicking his ears flat against his head the black cat furtively cast round for some reassurance that all wasn't as bad as it smelt, looked and felt. But he was deluding himself. It was all but yelling at him. Hairless ape had passed this way.

"How unworthy of the mighty hunter……"

the panther's thoughts - or was it the wind - quipped back,

"for was it not on your own paws, fleet and strong, you arrived at this place? It's as well cats are inquisitive and can't resist a challenge. Go, see for yourself the work of these hairless apes…...."

thought, or *was* it the wind, trailed off momentarily, before whirling back with a rhetorical nudge,

"for have not Mothers nature and earth called you?!"

Indeed. Holding fast to that none too small conceit the panther steeled himself; then, sinuous and silent as a snake on the stalk, shimmied closer, insinuating his way with studied care, despite a burning conviction nothing could smell so bad and live. He wormed forward with infinite caution. After all: just as an antelope will feign a fall so to repel a challenge with a fatal thrust of its horns, some animals will play *potto* - play dead - lying in ambush to retaliate for an attack in which an injury was sustained, or for the death of a mate or offspring; buffalo and lion being cases in point. It was soon apparent that the body squatted lifelessly against the tree was the old silverback, the one he'd first laid eyes on little over a sunrise ago. His first notion was that it had been beaten in a battle for supremacy by a younger contender, perhaps the other silverback in the gully. Of this he was quickly disillusioned. The corpse of this gorilla was headless.

A bloodied, gagging hole of hacked flesh, muscle and bone gaped back at the panther. The huge, domed head looked to have been ripped from the silverback's massive shoulders, as if no more than a fragile flower-head plucked from its stem. Riverlets of blood trailed forlornly down the muscular immensity of the gorilla's chest to where two neat holes, each no bigger than a cheetah's spot, drew the panther's eye. They were indents no more than what a bushbuck's horns would make. Umbulala focused wider. Above a congealed puddle of blood blotting the flattened grass between the apes' legs, two mighty arms -

their rich, dew-dappled fur still in shining condition - hung loose, with the wrists of each gaunt and bloodied from where the mitt-like hands had been hacked off. Just like the head. A scowl creased Umbulala's ebony face.

Swerving round, as if suddenly coming under attack, the big cat yawled into the wind:

"Why?? Why do these hairless ones take only heads and paws? Where's the wisdom in killing something so huge.....for so little?"

Difficult it certainly is to believe why a predator would kill for just a few 'parts', and leave behind such a monstrous bulk of meat. To the panther it went beyond all bounds of what was reasonable. He plumped down on the ground nonplussed, head thrust back, nostrils flared, peering at the grotesque remains of the once majestic gorilla.

"Who knows...."

a caressing breeze soughed softly back

"for since time immemorial have I wandered the jungle, and of all nature's creatures, from those that swim, to the birds of the air to all that wriggle or walk earth's surface these hairless ones....." so it seemed to sigh, "are the most ruthless, their frequently fiendish, usually short-sighted ways impossible to fathom by any logical rationale."

Having heard much the same all before, even seen for himself something of the scourge of hairless ape in another place and time, it was still difficult for Umbulala to find the remotest sense in any of it. The concept of killing just to 'steal' from a gorilla its head, from an elephant its foot, from a dainty dikdik its skull and tiny crown of horns - even, recalling Sibindi, the very skin in which an animal walks the jungle - was to the big cat beyond any rightful law of nature, and for that matter, comprehension. He turned, looking hard at the holes in the gorilla's chest:

"These must be from their sticks of fire, the kind that tore at the leg of Bulala. They look so insignificant....." he grunted in disbelief, "as if made by a small antelope's horns, and surely hardly enough to take such a prodigiously powerful life!"

A breeze, urgently whisking through the lichen and fern strung branches, appeared to whine back:

"Go look behind……where it's almost as if Inyati the buffalo has kicked it out from the inside. Nothing: plant, insect, fish, reptile, bird or beast, great or modest, is immune to the destructive wiles of the hairless ones. Even earth's waterways, mountains, forests - the very air - are tamed and diverted, ripped asunder, poisoned. Come to their hide lower down the slopes, a little way from where the rushing waterfalls plunge their sparkle over the rockface to the glimmering lake below; there's more to see, and they're not around."

Umbulala was only too glad to. He might well fear for his own hide, given the capacity of these hairless ones for wanton acquisition; acquisition not remotely tempered by such basics as efficiency, a code of behaviour or some *scratch-my-back* ethos that holds true for all higher animals. Soberly he took his leave.

The panther made steady progress toward the place of the waterfalls. He was careful to keep moving into the wind, all the while guided by the scents and sounds that floated by on the back of it; with, every increasingly among them, the musky, sweet-sour odour of hairless ape leading him on, inexorably and eventually, to their hideout deep in the forest. Umbulala halted at the edge of a stand of nettles, viciously slashed and pushed aside to form a path. Their covert was tucked just beyond in a clearing. A huge tree loomed up to one side. It was an aged Hagenia, coincidentally of the same type under which, in mocking irony, the carcass of the silverback remained profanely propped; only the massive bole of this one was hollow. Many small animals, from genets to hyraxes, make lodgings or caches of these ancient, cavernous trees; the hairless apes had appropriated this strapping specimen for their own purposes, utilizing it in much the same way for stowage, and probably more besides.

Yet by far the most compelling sight for Umbulala was what he took to be another shelter, or dry den in the centre of the clearing. Big enough to take several hairless apes, it was very likely only used by the dominant ape or apes; the other or others being relegated to the more humble refuge of the Hagenia tree to the side of the clearing. Formed first of saplings twisted together, then woven through with large, soft leaves and tied at the top, it had all the look and shape of a large conical nest, reminiscent of those that some birds make; only many times bigger. The site was otherwise bare and deserted....with just midway between the shelters, a ring of rocks encircling a smouldering fire.

Hovering where the undergrowth ended and the clearing began, Umbulala's thoughts and eyes were gripped. Cocking his head to one side - as if seeking explanations of all he was seeing - the big cats' searching gaze strayed to the fire. Twirling up from its embers like a wispy question mark was a lonely trail of grey-blue smoke about which a breeze twisted and teased: *hairless apes are the only creatures driven out of need to tame fire*. Umbulala shook himself into movement - and stealthily slinked into the clearing.

He began to pad and sniff about warily so to get the measure of these hairless apes. Taking constant note of the wind, he moved with the vigilance of one intending not to leave a trace of himself, treading on stones and clumps of grass, alert to every twist and turn; careful not to brush against anything and inadvertently leave his scent behind. For some reason he peered up at the top of the hairless apes' den of leaves and stems - only to be startled by the unexpected sight of a face leering down at him. In an involuntary reaction the alarmed panther stepped back a pace or two, glowering and spitting up at it, ready to defend himself. In so doing he unwittingly trod in a patch of mud, leaving behind the perfect imprint of a hind paw. With his attention gripped as it was, the big cat was unaware of his slip.

Hanging above the shelter's opening was the severed head of the gorilla, its mouth frozen open in a death grimace; either side, as in some grim ritual, drooped two huge hands like petrified mitts. In the surprise of the moment, the big cat's ready summation that hairless apes must hang their kills like leopards to return to when hunger bites, is understandable. Only too quickly was he relieved of this more 'reassuring' notion when he thought he heard, weeping faintly away on the breeze:

"Not so hunter of the night. The head and hands are drying as *trophies* of their so-called hunt; to show-off to others of their kind; to bedeck their dens…." the chill litany ran on, "to extract even the teeth to hang upon themselves."

Learning all he needed, or wanted to, Umbulala sombrely slipped away through the cover of trees and underbrush flanking the clearing, off in the direction of a rocky scarp he'd earlier noted jutting above the line of vegetation.

It lay just beyond a towering bank of nettles. Tall as young giraffes, these plants little worry most animals - gorillas chomp through the spindly stuff in bundles, even construct nests with it - yet, as he'd seen at the lair, hairless apes take virulent objection to it; due, maybe, to some lost protective reaction. The big cat scurried up onto a ledge, then on again to a cleft higher up the rockface which, while out of sight from below, offered a bird's eye view of the hideout. Making himself comfortable he set about cleaning himself, a matter of course that brought with it the opportunity for some forward-planning. But meditation and relaxation were short-lived when, with the stomach-churning realisation of his error, he found it - mud caked between the claws and over the pad of one hind paw. It meant only one thing……and the big cat admonished himself with a curt snipe:

"AAaggrrr....I've left my mark behind...." then as quickly again wondered "but will they notice it?" the thinking being if they did, how swiftly would any identify it.

His thoughts raced. Here surely was a test of how wise these hairless apes were, hardly daring to hope his pug wouldn't be found. Yet he hadn't the luxury of choice. After what they did to Bulala, *Sibindi* - the big panther groaned feverishly under his breath, casting a wistful look round - the bongo, now this fine gorilla, it was fair to conclude this was not the place to relax. It didn't take a great leap of imagination: if they picked up Umbulala's pug, they'd next be after him! And with this operative notion now dictating action, the panther slipped unobtrusively down from his lookout - his aim to find asylum in an interim sanctuary further round the mountain slopes, while making certain he left in the course of his passage a trail convoluted enough to bamboozle any foes fate might chance to set on his track.

Buffalo

LEAVES ON THE WIND

The mountain grass is singing kyries to the skies

ecreted snugly away in its serene solitude, Umbulala lay among the ample boughs of a white-flowering *Pygeum* tree, a forest giant as much at home on its own on ridges or the edges of ravines, as in stands of mixed, mountain woodland. Sought after for the blue berries that festoon it in its brief fruiting season, its appeal belies the acrid odour its bark gives out when cut; or, indeed, when scored by sharp curved claws. From such has the tree's humbling yet apt sobriquet Stinkwood derived.

Perfectly camouflaged under its canopy from where he had an excellent prospect out, while none could readily see in, Umbulala - rather like a mother leopard quite done with the trials of jungle life, the hunt and on-going demands of cubs - had had quite enough of late, ending as it had with that severed gorilla's head. What with this, all that had preceded it, then the chastening discovery that he'd left his pugmark behind, the big cat had prudently opted to put as much space between himself and the hairless apes. Yet surprise hadn't played itself out; another memorable encounter was waiting in the wings, this one bright of eye, sharp of wit and with a talent that would take his breath away.

Dozily stretched out in his shady nook overlooking a secluded forest pool, Umbulala was his most relaxed since he'd first sighted the gorillas in the gully; only a few sunrises past, yet now seemingly moons back. Tucked away in a wooded glade, the pool was an alluring draw for a mix of fauna, due in no small part to it being charmingly cloistered mid a splendid grove of trees. Hung with trails of wispy lichen, many were linked over the pool by lianas and vines, natural ropeways that only enhanced its ambience. From these jungle catwalks monkeys dangled, deftly scooping up watery mouthfuls as if born to it; in sun-kissed patches bee-eaters, sunbirds and butterflies like tiny prisms of iridescence flashing to and fro, flitted and shimmered; frothy banks of ferns and flowering shrubs fussed about the pool edges, while splashing down into it over a stony slope weathered smooth with the flow was a silvery spring, the quartzy lustre of the rock beneath winking through a sheen of water clear as mountain air.

Into this blissful serenity stepped a slender cat. Half the size again of a young leopardess, markedly shorter of tail too, Umbulala recognized a serval. But this one, oddly so in his experience, was black all over, just like him, making a naturally leggy cat even lankier. With less of the 'frown' of its spotted relatives, yet still possessed of their alert upstanding ears, so-shaped like great oval shells to catch the tiniest sound, the lissom cat tripped daintily down to drink. Any impulse to intrude, if one existed, was not in Umbulala's ambit. Other issues weighed too heavily, and he couldn't have chanced upon a more beatific retreat to ponder how best to approach what loomed. Tranquillity was sorely needed to knit together some rational plan of defence, or attack. It wasn't to be.

Tranquillity fled as fleetingly as feathers on a fore-wind when in a jarring blast of cacophony and colour an unabashedly noisy party of tree-dwelling Turacos landed nearby. Lustrous olive and violet livery vividly offset by white facial flashes and scarlet flight feathers firmly places these glossy denizens of mountain forest among its more dazzling habitués. Yet for all their visual charm any aesthetic appreciation of Turaco pulchritude - let alone forgiving notions of where beauty attaches, hooliganism is pardoned - could not be further from the mental orbit of one very decidedly, very rudely jolted Umbulala.

A gentle breeze wafting by appeared to confirm them as distant cousins of some similarly intrusive birds with which Umbulala was well acquainted from his hunting grounds down country: the Grey louries, or as they're better known thereabouts in deference to their meddlesome ways, *G'way* birds. One simply couldn't avoid the presence of these turacos either; hence he didn't doubt the connection for a moment. They even shared with louries the vexing habit of pretentiously hopping from one branch to another - for no apparent reason, or so it seems, other than to show-off - before scurrying at speed up a branch to its tip, one startle-eyed head after another straining to be first to whatever succulent inducement might be dangling there. The panther was determined to ignore the pandemonium. Forcing his eyes tight shut he lay motionless - the consummate cool cat above it all, legs hung loose, head leant casually against a branch. The intention was to present a picture of bored nonchalance, and as such profess total disinterest in the rowdy goings-on; an intention that didn't count on the rude intrusion of the totally unexpected. It's amazing how a sound out of nowhere can cut across the noisiest atmosphere to the point of shattering the senses. So it was now when a voice like that of hairless ape suddenly screeched above the prattle: "Who's a pretty boy then!"

Never in the panther's life, maybe never in the history of leopards, did he get such a shock: one all-consuming, heart-stopping, blood-chilling fright all-in-one! The big cat sprang to his feet with a desperate cough of alarm, smashing his skull on the upper branch as he did. Darting wild glances about for the dastardly hairless ape who'd dare sneak up undetected, and unbidden, the panther's lips curled back in a full-throated snarl. Already the turacos had taken wing in alarm. But no hairless ape did he sight, nor scent. Only he remained, a picture of abject unease in the Stinkwood....and some way up in its topmost

branches, a grey-feathered bird with a red tail. With a curved beak perfect for cracking nuts, it peered down through the foliage. Two black eyes, set like shiny paw-paw pips in swirls of yellow, were beadily measuring up the scowling panther when all at once the thick beak squawked again with shivering effect:

"The turacos, in showing me the ways of the jungle, acclaimed the cat in the tree was the mighty Umbulala who fears nothing! But….." cocking its head in that assured, inquiring way of parrots, "Brother wind said that while you are indeed brave, you have one fear - the ones without feathers or fur who walk upright like the herons and marabous. Clearly I upset your equilibrium with my *pretty boy* call", it teased, "which never fails!"

Still agitated - as the parrot had observed with maddening accuracy - and not a little confounded, Umbulala was relieved; relieved beyond belief to be confronting, not hairless ape, but a bird with a skill comparable to nothing he'd come across. Managing to regain some dignity the panther controlled an agitated groan, and gritting his teeth, sizzled instead through clenched jaws that left nothing in earshot in doubt:

"Never do that again parrot! It's the kind of scheming, pesky thing Brother wind would do. I thought birds the size of francolins and sandgrouse weren't too clever - but you, little sister…." he mewled in awe "you have skill, curiosity, a true daughter of the jungle. And I do fear the hairless ones…with good reason. But why, and, *how* did you learn to imitate the sounds they make, and so convincingly? Like you, I too want to know all things about the jungle."

As the panther, composing himself little by little, gradually reclined back on his branch, the parrot, in turn, nattily puffed out her soft grey feathers in one, smooth motion. Letting them settle neatly back in place, so unfolded the sober tale of a spirited bird:

"I was abducted from a nest high in a hole in a forest tree by a hairless ape."

Her feathers hadn't yet grown so she couldn't fly; she could only beg for food from her elders just like the other parrots taken with her; so crammed together they could barely breath:

"They put us in a kind of snare shaped like the nest of a weaver bird, but larger, and without an opening through which to escape; it was made of grass so closely woven none could break free. I could hardly move a feather it was so crushed inside, and soon many stopped breathing. Only I lived......".

They fed her and gave her water, and in time her wing feathers appeared. But when these grew long and fine they cut the pinions, so still she couldn't fly. The parrot's timbre turned doleful:

"Sad it is, for I no longer know where my kin live; I am a stranger to the jungle because the hairless apes carried me far away, down into the lowlands, to those parts where there are no great rambling forests of trees, and no parrots like me. There I was put in their den, like a cave cool and dark."

Her cage was hung on a verandah; sometimes it was taken inside where mounted heads of animals lined the walls:

"But none called out to me; all just stared lifelessly ahead...." she paused, blinking twice, as if conjuring up the very atmosphere of it, "and there the hairless apes taught me to make the sounds they make. To do this they would cover me over, taking away the light, dissolving day instantly to night."

For one who is a worshipper of all that is bright, it was suddenly dark, yet the sun was still high in the sky. The parrot scratched her head at the contradiction:

"They would repeat over and over the same, meaningless utterances until it drove me to distraction. It was then I decided to try to make them back - to see how it bored them! To my astonishment they'd remove the cover when I did this, and the light again streamed in. Soon they didn't even bother; I just repeated whatever noises they made. It was better to speak their tongue and see the sun, than exist forever in lifeless gloom."

The parrot squinted, and switching her gaze the opposite way - perhaps to get a different slant on the cat - squawked more cheerily:

"In time my wing feathers grew back...." and with it a chance to escape that arose unexpectedly. "Some hairless apes came to the den; they were not welcome, and soon those with whom I lived turned angry. When they all began to smell of fear, there followed much banging and running about, their sticks of fire flashing and searing the air. My nest fell to the ground in the turmoil. It broke open and I fled, burrowing myself in a bougainvillaea, as the hairless apes call it, creeping over a small Acacia tree where I hid among its blaze of colour. In all this time I had never taken to the air; thus I was a clumsy flyer. But land I did, held on to my freedom and watched."

The parrot stopped, agitatedly hopping up and down, and shaking her head:

"Eventually only two of the hairless ones were left standing - two of those who came uninvited to the den - and just before making away they did something most odd: they set fire free to wantonly ravage and burn. And soon from inside the den came the dying cries of my hairless ones. They next did something even stranger, something this humble parrot will never understand - they slew all the animals and other birds that lived there, the dogs and horses, even those that gave freely of their milk and eggs; nothing was spared - nothing.....not even the wails and bellows of the dying; except me, hiding and trembling among the blossoms."

She moved from side to side in that familiar swaying motion of parrots, gazing fixedly, not a little disturbed by the memory of it all:

"So if what Brother wind tells me is true" she rasped "you might need my modest help. It is yours, for I am with you!"

At this the Grey parrot flew off in search of food. She was the first of her kind he'd encountered, yet her tale determined him to have done with these hairless apes once and for all. It also inspired something else, something of perhaps far greater worth. Unbeknown to the parrot she had indirectly confirmed in the panther a method of approach, the seed of which had been steadily taking root: a tactic, obvious in its simplicity, which could be pivotal to his whole strategy. Here clearly was a bird with a mind of her own. Unlike most her size, who dip and sway as if unsure where they're flying, even her flight was straight and to the point. The panther must do the precise opposite - plot not a straight, but a twisted trail, a deceiving web, and in so doing ensnare the hairless apes in their own, devious ways.

And so the reckoning began. Umbulala immediately made for the lake at the base of the falls. The way there took him over a sprawling plateau where, at some point past, the ground to one side had given way in a landslide. A sheer cliff face had formed, and from its topmost edge an eye-level view opened out right across a wide sweep of the tree canopy, to give a rare close-up of the upper storey of the high forest. Umbulala gazed over a swell of frondescence, dimpled with breezes and birds dipping in and out. At least he presumed they were birds - until drawn to a part of the forest below. Here something curious was going on, and it seemed, at first glance, neither bird nor bat related. Small leaf-like things, one or two now and then, would float between the trees. Not bright splashes of colour, just a soft grey-brown. The panther's gut reaction was, if they were not tiny birds, nor bats, perhaps they were large moths; failing that, leaves. But these were too life-like to be mere leaves; as for moths......! He then noticed a few more. But these weren't floating at irregular intervals through the air, but adroitly gliding up a tree trunk, only to disappear into a hollow in the wood. Finally one landed on a branch directly below him.

Clearly visible from where he looked down, he focused in. It wasn't a bird, a bat, nor a moth. It was a tiny furred animal, somewhat like a mouse, but with larger eyes and ears, very long whiskers, and a sweeping, bristled tail rather like a single feather longer than its entire head and body. And it was lying so close to the wood it didn't even cast a shadow! Umbulala caught his breath - such a grace that, not to cast a shadow. What wouldn't he give to have such a gift for what he was about to embark on - to use at any moment of choosing, wherever and whenever. What the cat was gazing on were Pygmy flying squirrels, tiniest of their kind. Indeed so small were they, one could fit inside a goose egg, with room left over to scratch itself! They seemed shy of exposing themselves too long in the open, almost rushing into the hole in the tree trunk. He guessed from this they might be mostly nocturnal, which didn't preclude them being seen in daylight; in fact, he'd go so far as to reckon these flying squirrels saw as well by day, as by night. Flaps of skin joining their front and back legs caught the breeze, enabling the squirrels to fly - or rather glide like leaves on the wind. Lowering or heightening a leg either side to control their direction they'd effortlessly float through the air several elephant's lengths. But this wasn't the end to the marvel of it.

Umbulala wasn't unaccustomed to flying squirrels; yet down country they were bigger. So naturally when a squirrel first alighted on the branch his first impression was that he was looking at a cub of its type. But when it was joined by another of like-size the two mated, disillusioning him there and then of any such notions! This size differential thing intrigued him. Up here what was bigger elsewhere - elephants and buffaloes - came up smaller; while what one least expected - pigs and monkeys - came up giants! Colour was also an issue.

Generally it was all or mostly black, as notable with gorillas, chimps - Giant hog too, and he shuddered at the recollection - or the chestnut-red, of some description, of Forest duikers, Red river hogs and bushbuck, all the way to Forest buffalo and bongo. These forests were more and more an enigma to him. But that's the genius of nature: dexterous of wit and craft, capturing his curiosity to cleverly, subtly, draw him more and more in, until he was one with it.

Remnant of volcanic activity aeons back, the lake was no less alluring. With its clean elliptical shape, neatly set under an endless, sheltering sky between the encircling hills of the rift escarpment, it was like a great crystal eye watching over the forests and mountains around and above it. The lake bounds were noticeably different to higher up the slopes. Vegetation dotted the shoreline. But where clutches of palms and bananas weren't vying for attention, galleries of swaying papyrus and reeds fringed inviting strips of sand on which life, terrestrial and aerial, came and went. Umbulala secreted himself away in a position perfect for gazing across one such stretch. Out on the lake tiny islets, like reedy whalebacks of rock, played host to cormorants and other water birds; ibises and shoebills

waded and fed in the shallows close by; while just below a nearby bluff, a herd of elephant bathed. Some were lazily sucking up trunkfuls of the lake as others slapped their hides with leafy stems and fronds to brush away insects and similar

irritants. Two youngsters - one half-grown, the other a small calf - were further out in the water.

The older calf, well up to its shoulders, was keenly eyeing its little confrere struggling to keep up. When the latter predictably dropped beneath the surface with just its lifeline proboscis waving overhead like the questing antenna of some submerged crustacean, the older calf reached forward - and with its own trunk promptly pushed the littler one under the water. A whirlpool of churning, bubbling rebellion ensued, followed by a tiny, distraught, elephantine shape surging backwards to the safety of the shallows, spluttering and heaving as a disapproving aunt advanced, waving an admonishing branch at the persecutor. Though smaller than the savanna giant, these round-eared Forest elephants - Umbulala had only previously heard feeding in the bamboo higher up the slopes and never seen - still clearly shared with their bigger bush relatives the same capacity for mischief, not least a penchant for playing tricks! And as a comic picture flashed to mind of a buffalo horns over hooves in a waterhole - brunt of a cheeky, rearguard surprise by a young elephant squealing with delight as its bundled off by an unamused Matriarch - Umbulala's gaze wandered skyward.

White-throated blue swallows were darting and shooting in and about the nearby papyrus. Drawn by the multitude of insects that thronged it, the thread-

like heads of the tall grass were harbours of rest the swallows would only alight on when light fell, their feast of flying all done until the following sunrise. Marvelling at how in one svelte movement the slim, sleek forms - like tranches of tropic sky - would slip in and out the tall galleries of papyrus, skim the water and scoop up a drink in flight, the big cat coughed a greeting:

"Why so few of you this year little brothers and sisters - have those master hunters of the air, the buzzards and bat-hawks, cut a swathe through you?"

Seemingly in one they twittered back:

"No......just the hairless ones: they kill the insects we feed on; while others of their ilk slay us in flight with their sticks of fire as we cross the endless swathe of water many, many moons beyond the jungle - where from far below, from what look like harmless lily-pads of earth dotting a vast lagoon, they smite and blast us from the skies like no gentle lily could ever do. Mother nature gives us the skill and wit to fly to faraway places, only to fall like dying leaves from a tree. Such accursed creatures are these hairless apes!"

Umbulala crooned in empathy, before wondering aloud if they had ever come across in their wanderings Grey parrots with red tails, and where. On tiny beating wings a swallow warbled back:

"So - are you now after eating parrots mighty panther?!"

Gazing up in unbridled admiration of such avian art - if a leopard could but fly so, it would be master over all - a reflective Umbulala snorted lightly:

"No, little sister, but I know one such Grey parrot who wants to glean all she can about her kinfolk. She knows only the lowlands to where the hairless apes spirited her away, clipping her wings and taking away the light and freedom of flight rightfully hers."

And as the swallows banked away with masterly ease, there wafted back on the breeze: *Follow the setting sun - then will she come to the land of Grey parrots.*

It was the cue for Umbulala to move off too; more or less go back on himself, but by a slightly different route, and in so doing continue to work a tangled trail. Of this the cat was ever mindful as he slinked through the deep cover skirting the lakeside.   Stealing away through banks of undergrowth and the shadowy overhang of trees edging the water margins, he lifted his snout to check ahead.....and grimaced. Sensitive nostrils scented on the wind a distant presence. It wasn't one he welcomed, and though accept its existence he must, the big cat spat defiantly into the wind. It wasn't the scent of any jungle creature; it was that of hairless ape - and it would forever be too close for comfort, whatever the distance between.

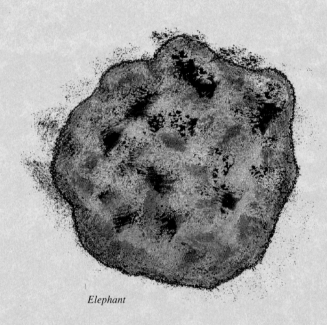

Elephant

CAST NO SHADOW

*As mighty in its way as the giants of the
jungle, the dung beetle rolls all before it!*

The panther had taken out a duiker in the small hours. Now as dawn softly broke over the high country, he rested along the upper boughs of a tall Olive tree; his paws curled neatly under him, his thickly furred tail coiled round as a windbreak against the crisp air of early morn. With hairless ape somewhere in the vicinity, the big leopard had prudently tucked himself away in the Olive tree's heavy foliage; foliage also ideal, as the light lifted, for hiding and shading the remains of the kill he'd stashed in the upper branches. The comforting conviction no creature knew he was there was soon scattered to the winds with a sudden bustle in the lower branches announcing the arrival of the Grey parrot. Peering up through a web of limb and leaf she moved her head from side to side, examining every patch, before letting out a low squawk, just enough to draw the panther's attention:

"Brother panther! Mighty hunter with the hide of night somewhere in the branches above - 'tis I, Grey parrot!"

The soft cough of leopard cut back through the dappled shadows, quite from where she couldn't tell:

"Sister parrot...." it appeared to paradoxically float from the foliage where the parrot had landed, "what news?"

It is contradictions such as this, this very confusion of source, which marks the master hunter from the mediocre. The Grey parrot cocked her head, first to one side than the other:

They've found it!" she gravely cawed. "They've found your pug, and two of the hairless apes, one with pale skin like those in whose den I lived, announced it was lion by the mere fact of its size! But for the brown wizened one with bent legs, wiser in the ways of the jungle, it could only belong to the 'chief' of all leopards whose coat, it was claimed, would be much coveted by hairless ape - to wear as a symbol of power or hang in a den - boasting it would soon no longer be yours; likewise the heads and hands of more great apes. They plan to hunt gorilla at the next sunrise."

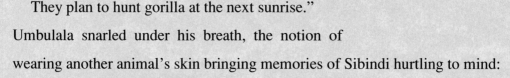

Umbulala snarled under his breath, the notion of wearing another animal's skin bringing memories of Sibindi hurtling to mind:

"Well - I must not disappoint them........"

and as he slipped down the tree without the bird catching a glimpse of his going, there floated up a parting message of special resonance for the Grey parrot:

"Oh, and little sister..." it appeared to croon, "the swallows tell me that if you follow the setting sun, you will soon be in the land of Grey parrots."

After a distance the panther gratefully stumbled on the more open stretch of a game path. Looking to have been furrowed out over time by the hooves of countless Forest buffalo, it at last enabled him to move with greater ease without the constant impediment of a choking net of plant life catching at every part of him. He soon came to a tree with a trunk of such huge proportions its supporting buttresses straddled the trail. What next greeted his eye was a vision of pure beauty. Ahead stretched a vast patch of moist ground - running on for python lengths too innumerable to figure - seemingly layered from edge to edge in a mantle of gossamer-like flowers. It crossed the cat's mind that a mass of tree orchids had shed their petals all in the same moment, sprinkling them lavishly over the ground below, until it was covered in a spread of pastel splendour. But all wasn't what it seemed. The petals, instead of lying flat as in a bed of fallen leaves, were standing virtually upright, each quivering slightly and overlapping its neighbour - as in a pangolin's coat of scales - but haphazardly so. It was enough to completely block out the ground beneath.

As the panther stepped lightly into this gentle, shimmering florescence it melded in a heartbeat into a spellbinding kaleidoscope of life swirling everywhere about him. Suddenly, and silently, fluttering upward in a multi-hued cloud, the petals metamorphized into wings that opened out into a spectacle of butterflies. Rising up from their lighting-spots on the damp earth where they'd been sucking up minerals, Umbulala moved softly through a swelling rainbow of colour. Like myriad blossoms dancing in the air, they floated in and out the shafts of sunlight piercing the treetops, alighting back on the ground the moment he passed to sup more from the soil, especially from around the fresh pugmarks. Never had Umbulala seen such a pageant of butterflies in a single place: a veritable symphony of yellow, black and white, oranges and reddish pinks shot through with turquoise and mauve, and in such profusion that at one point they simultaneously blanketed out the game trail and the view of the forest beyond.

Passing through the last of the butterflies, the entranced cat roused himself from his reverie. He quickened his pace; as he did a layer of leaves ahead began to first churn, then whirl and pirouette with demonic energy down the trail toward him. Taken by a swirling wind gust, they spun nearer and nearer, gaining momentum and leaves with every twirl and turn, until he thought he could hear through the susurrous swish of their leafy rustle a breeze whining a warning note his way: *hairless ape is on your trail - the brown, wizened one wise in the way of the jungle; the others sleep in their den.* The panther skidded softly to a halt. Holding his head pensively to one side, he let slip a sharp *gnarr* in protest at the turmoil of thought now crowding it; thoughts, such as if they came one by one, it would better his chances; how, as he caught sight of his shadow in the deepening sunshine, it would be sweet indeed to cast no shadow; and, if he was to keep to his vow to taste neither blood nor flesh of hairless ape, a means of diversion - an ally even - could well be the missing piece that ensured it. Umbulala sighed, ever the realist. Such notions were fantasy he couldn't afford investing the vaguest hope in.

"Per-hap*sssss* I can help…..cat of the night!"

A long, wheezy *sissss* - like air whooshing down a hollow stalk - drifted over from an outcrop of lichen-covered boulders, its base fringed by grass and shrubbery. Emanating from beyond a clump of reeds bent and flattened by a heavy animal, the panther shot a glance in its direction. Cautiously turning face-on to it, he fell into a crouch; a wingbeat later the superlative, probing vision of the felid had picked out a slender, snakelike object flicking in and out. He quickly recognised the long, forked tongue of an egg-loving reptile frequently met anywhere there's a river, creek or waterhole - more so if there's a rocky outcrop or kopje about, stony cavities being favoured refuges. It was a Water monitor, a lizard supreme among its kind.

"Ho! Brother leguaan…." the big cat crooned a greeting, "hairless apes, in whose lair up the slopes hangs the head and hands of the mighty silverback, are about to work more shameless misdeeds. I've been charged with stopping them; an ally in this would be a gift indeed."

As long as a leopard is long, its imperious head held high on a long, sturdy neck, a Water monitor of huge proportions swaggered into the open. With the alert eyes and steely gaze of the hunter emblazoned across it, the olive-green hide of the handsome lizard, faintly speckled yellow and black, glinted in the light. It lashed its heavy ridged tail aside; then, swivelling round with a deftness belied by its shape, pointed down the trail with its snout to an abandoned anthill near the riverbank. Here lived the Spitting cobra:

"Kafula will join us....her aversion to hairless apes is legendary."

The monitor was already leading off, well on the way, exemplar forked tongue enthusiastically tasting the air. The panther responded with alacrity. That there's safety in numbers can be no truer adage. His skin too was at stake. Readily keeping up with the big reptile, the panther was impressed by the nifty pace it made, given its clumsy waddling gait. Yet ever the master hunter Umbulala didn't forget the essentials of bushcraft. Despite the tempo they were keeping, he made certain he stopped every four buffalo lengths or so. This was not only to check for hairless ape, but to intentionally temper his stride to assure enough of a gap was kept between his and the leguaan's tracks for it not to look suspect. Not only that. It was critical that he left sufficient scent and sign along the way, while appearing to move quite normally. This was to ensure that any hairless ape tracking his spoor should note nothing in his manner which might give the merest hint the hunted knew he was being hunted.

This was the hope. The difficulty is judging when enough is enough before it begins to look suspiciously unnatural. Overdoing it can be as fatal in moments of extremity as underestimating the opposition. Vindication of this, one of the basic tenets of survival, came in the course of discharging that very task - leaving behind his mark. Deliberately brushing against a branch jutting out across the game path to leave a trace of scent, and perhaps a touch of fur, an urgent breeze whizzing through its foliage, something in its timbre - sounding an advisory, as much as an affirmatory note - caught the panther's ear. The bent and wizened one might move slowly but nothing was missed, the essence of it seemed to run; hence he was prudent to proceed as much in character as possible while remaining wise to the strong and weak points of the foe, shrewdly knowing when it was expedient to make play with them, and balancing plans accordingly. The monitor halted at the base of a towering termite mound, with a medley of palms and ferns to one side, a strapping Euphorbia, ancient of aspect, to the other. At some stage in the past its white ant community had abandoned the tall termitarium. Veteran of many generations use, huge mushrooms like great white flowers sprouted in places from its outer crust.

Now a new occupant was in residence. In the mound wall, just about at Umbulala's shoulder height, there was an opening roughly the size of an ostrich egg. The big lizard, lifting its head level with the hole, called in a low rasp:

"*Kafula* - feared and admired by the wise: we fellow hunters of the jungle seek Sister cobra's help in repelling the hairless one."

Moments slipped by. Then, not long after a tiny movement in the darkened hole betrayed a presence, the head and banded neck of a Spitting cobra oozed into the sunlight. Lifting her head and spreading her narrow hood - more for effect in this instance than threat - she hissed back:

"Only fools.....or the very brave seek out the Spitting cobra. I suspect you both fall into the last category. So.......what need has Brother leguaan and Umbulala for the likes of Kafula?!"

The panther squatted; then with a low, complicitous purr only they were privy to, quietly and softly unveiled a cunning strategy to deal with the hairless one tailing him - now assured by fresh spoor, in the way of tracks of pugs and other sign he'd left along the trail - flicking his gaze back and forth between the monitor and the snake, not a little wary of being mesmerized by the cobra keeping up an hypnotic, swaying motion of her head. The monitor was to hide under a bush roughly opposite the mound. Umbulala would circle round to come up behind the ape whose attention he'd then draw with the most spine-chilling, screaming roar he could muster - the signal for the monitor to go on to demonstrate why its kind are respected by the judicious throughout the jungle as *leguaans* - the 'leg-breakers'.

   "With just a swipe of your tail you must knock out at least one scrawny leg of
   the hairless one. If you fail...."
the big cat grunted soberly

   "you will be killed before Sister cobra
   or I can come to your aid. Falling in
   front of the anthill, Kafula will be there,
   ready to incapacitate the hairless one
   further; as the ape struggles back from a
   blinding burst of searing venom - I'll
   be waiting."

   Gracefully lowering her hood the cobra
hissed approval.....and avowed collusion.
Suspecting the hairless ape would soon be
upon them, all parties now took to cover.
The monitor lizard headed for a tangle of bush, there to position itself, directed all the while by the cobra and panther as to the best spot from which to angle a strike without risking being seen first. The cobra slid back into her hole in the anthill to await the approaching moment. Meantime Umbulala, careful to leave no compromising sign of his passage, slithered silently off into the undergrowth flanking the trail, on through the concealing screen of green in the direction from which he anticipated the hairless ape would be coming, thence up behind an outcrop nestled in a shady thicket. It was set back conveniently enough from the trail, while commanding a clear view of it. All was ready.

It never ceased to mystify the panther how at grave moments of crisis, those turning points in life on which destiny revolves, everything slips into largo mode - the slow-motion tempo that's no cliché - of hushed anticipation when the silence seems almost to scream, when not even the trill of a bird intrudes. It's as if the wild is collectively holding its breath. Wondering if the hairless ape, if as wise as proclaimed, noticed it too, the faint sound of something approaching cut across the panther's consciousness. The hairless one, brown, wizened and bent as the Grey parrot had described, crept into view. Umbulala was staggered. What struck him first was the legs: not straight like those of the heron, but so bowed and gnarled, like old spindly branches, it was a wonder they stayed up! By contrast, the eyes of the hairless ape were darting everywhere. They were alive - not with fear but the cool concentration of the hunter, and quickly picked up on the faeces Umbulala had discreetly left, covered over just enough not to be missed by a trained observer. They weren't.

The old one stopped, and with a bare foot pushed the dung about, prodding it with a toe to gauge its freshness before stalking on, a little more eager of step. The panther nodded to himself: so far it was proceeding on target; how much longer was about to be rigorously tested. The hairless ape was now moving in the direction of the ant-heap from where the track, which Umbulala had earlier scouted, wound on to a swampy backwater with a creek coursing through it. For authenticity sake he'd left fresh spoor running a little distance along it beyond the termite mound, doubling back on himself through the undergrowth abutting it so not to leave a telltale set of return tracks. The cat slipped from behind the rocks, away through the rambling vegetation, thence up on to the game trail. The hunted now became the hunter.

The hairless ape came adjacent to the anthill and suddenly halted, hovering over the spoor of the monitor and the leopard, much taken by two quite disparate sets of the same freshness left by two such very different animals more or less in

176

the same place. However capricious, whatever the hairless ape was making of it, was now academic. The moment had come. Hacking across the silence an explosive *yawl*, intensifying instantaneously into a screaming roar, split the air like a thunderclap as the panther launched into a full charge along the game trail toward the termite mound. The hairless one spun round toward the roar, spear at the ready - only to be shocked rigid by the distant, yet horrifying prospect that was bearing down without any hint of changing tack. Hurtling ever closer in the fast-forward, zigzag motion leopards on the attack employ to confuse their quarry was a montrous black cat bigger than any leopard he'd encountered, face creased into a heinous snarl, fangs bared......more and more a menacing blur.

Worse followed in quick succession. The leguaan lurking in the vegetation whipped its ridged tail at the ape's legs, powering home against skin and bone in one crushing blow. On impact the ape fell sprawled in an agonized heap at the base of the anthill, spear flung from reach. Floundering around in a frantic bid to sit up, the old one came face to face with the next nightmare: a hooded Spitting cobra, swaying in motion with a soft, sibilant hiss that was fizzing menacingly through the hush, her gaze and aim fixed and ready:

"At lassssttt.....revenge for all the cobras, gaboon adders, horned vipers and others the hairless apes have slain, not because we may have harmed a hairless ape, but simply because we are here - stoned, and before dying, tossed on the flames to wriggle for our lives, a fate even our young aren't spared. So take this jungle juice...."

she spluttered, spitting a jet of venom straight at the startled face and eyes of the hairless ape

"in parting gift!"

The hairless ape recoiled in horror as the cobra scored a direct hit. It's curious how tenaciously one hangs onto life the nearer one comes to forfeiting it. Struggling in a delirium of agony up onto the leg still functioning reasonably, the old one began to hop and hobble down the trail, grabbing ahold of every vine and branch on the way that made an able prop - on, ever closer, toward the creek and, unwittingly, a hidden bluff which overhung it. In sobs of pain, half-blind, dazed, desperately dragging a fractured, possibly broken leg, the ape managed to stagger along - on a leg that had also sustained a share of the impact from the Leguaan's tail - at an increasingly wild and reckless pace. After all: through blurred vision a panther had passed like Brother death between a leguaan and the hooded head of a Spitting cobra as if it was the most natural thing in the world. Who, then, could blame the hairless one for seeing it as the jungle spirits turning against the old hunter, sending demon delusions to befuddle the senses with devilish trickery!

Suddenly, as if gripped by the kind of bewildered dementia that strikes when shock turns the head and makes creatures do ludicrous things, the old one began to go faster - too fast, too late, losing balance too close to the bluff to be able to arrest momentum, and tumbling down into the creek below. The fate of the one who would wear the skin of the 'chief of leopards' was sealed.

Halting in mid-spring, Umbulala looked down at the hairless ape lame and helpless below; the ape who'd boasted of taking the coat from his back. Beyond the shadows thrown by the trees on the bluff there sprawled a swampy patch where stands of tall grass and reeds flourished. Wind swept lazily through them, swaying the stems this way and that, in the process carrying the scent of hairless ape far and wide. A thicket suddenly parted and there stood a lone elephant, a bull with the demeanour of one who'd taken stock of the message on the wind. He moved across to the hairless one spread-eagled in the shallow water. Gazing down from the bluff the panther had no enthusiasm; nor, now, even the need to involve himself further; the elephant, clearly a veteran of many moons in the jungle, looked to be more than able to deliver the coup de grâce. It seemed as if the bull, sensing, indeed smelling fear, took the ape's presence as a challenge.

The bull was of the lesser known elephant variety he'd first seen down at the lake beyond the papyrus. Not the bigger savanna type: taller and more upright, with their broader ears and great tusks curved boldly forward - the latter being all very fine in open bush, but a hindrance in this thicker, richer, habitat with its preponderance of denser greenery and myriad hanging vines.

By obvious contrast, the smaller and markedly more compact Forest elephant here before him was ideal, the thinner tusks projecting downwards being better suited to easier carriage through the lusher vegetation, as well as for digging in the mineral rich ground. Yet - as like the elephants by the lake - this elephant, notwithstanding his solitary status, his long seasons alone in the jungle, remained an elephant, with all the markings of the elephant's temperament: formidable, and not to be taken lightly. This bull knew exactly what beckoned, and how to deal with it.

On reaching the hairless ape he knelt down on one knee; then without undue ceremony proceeded to crush the pelvis, before next thrusting a tusk, brown and scored with age, through the unfortunate ape's chest. Here was revenge for all the elephants needlessly, nay wastefully slaughtered and butchered; and not for their ivory, nor their hides alone, but for their feet, their ears and tails - even their penises, stuffed and given to hairless apes' mates for fun.

Who knows. This old bull elephant, living out his remaining days in his swampy jungle hermitage, eating of its lush grass and partaking of its plenitude of water and mud, wasn't telling. Some terrible darkness haunted his soul, and before Umbulala had realised it, he'd melted anonymously away - back into his reassuring, embracing cover of green.

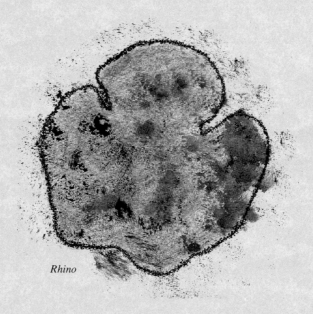

Rhino

SO SINGS THE BAMBOO

Rainbows are the smiles of a grateful land beaming back at the clouds

tretched along a jagged parapet of exposed rock jutting out over the sloping hillside, the panther watched the dawn peek like a shy cub over the mountaintops to slowly light up the jungle. A natural platform with a commanding view of the encircling slopes, glades and gullies frequented by the gorillas, it benefited by being largely screened off by a fall of foliage and bough that sheltered it well enough to baffle any observer looking on from outside. Umbulala had made good passage on the long trek back up from the creek to the area where he had last encountered gorillas, just one goal in mind: to arrive well before sunrise if he was to thwart the nefarious intentions of the remaining hairless apes. The despatch of the old wizened one - with due deference to the aid of unexpected collaborators and a third not even on a hastily assembled agenda - was an experience the big cat would long remember.

As light lifted, a loud burst of protracted *hoots* drew Umbulala's gaze along the slopes. Huge triple-storied bills, making them look farcically top-heavy, pied plumage and wings that 'sough' in flight - and a penchant, so said, for escorting monkeys on their travels - a showy flock of Black-and-White casqued hornbills taking noisily to the air is quite unmissable! Experience plausibly pointed to something startling them; *instinct* to it being out of sync with the preferred order of things. Focusing through a mesh of canopy and wispy mist, the cat's eyes honed in on movement below the treeline. A pattern began to emerge: there appeared to be two parallel lines of activity working their way along the slopes well below the treetops, and both at ground level. Following intently from his grand tier vantage point under its leafy overhang, a quirkiness, a certain rhythm in the rise and fall of the greenery in the lower storey, the relationship of movement to distance, soon came down to one thing: hairless apes!

Something was working its way through the cover of vegetation up the slope; meanwhile lower down, a hairless ape was just emerging into the open, flushing some Crested guineafowl from the undergrowth in the process. Vaguely comical under their shaggy-mop headcrests of thin, curly black feathers which bob about when they move, the birds bustled indignantly through the clearing with much wing-flapping and vocalising, then out again. On calm again descending, the hairless ape crossed to a clutch of shrubbery and trees and once there, as best Umbulala could decipher from his lookout, proceeded to fuss around with some branches, twigs and reeds.

Carefully bending a sapling over, the ape went on to attach to it what looked like a long vine, before pulling it taut, running it across to a stump opposite, catching it in a notch with a short twig sticking out crosswise, thence on again to a tree further back; the finishing stroke, the trigger, was a simple reed just leant at an oblique slant against the twig. The panther guessed what was astir. While the hairless one up the slope watched for gorillas, the accomplice in the clearing was setting a trap. Circling round they'd manoeuvre the unsuspecting apes into an ambush, presumably to ensnare the gorilla always to the fore of the group: the protector and leader they follow everywhere, the dominant silverback.

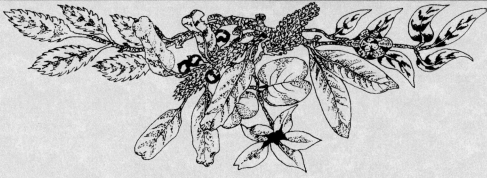

The panther carefully raised himself onto his haunches. Never once letting his eyes stray from the scene the cat cupped his ears forward, listening to every message on the wind as it swept by:

"It takes a hunter to catch a hunter. Wisdom…" it seemed to murmur "will be master here. Miss nothing. When the sun has covered the jungle completely in its light either they, or you, must be dead!"

Umbulala fell into a crouch. Swishing his tail down with a soft 'thwack' the big leopard shook his head in mock irritation. Such a chill prediction he could well do without. But sobering it remained. His thoughts began to race, searching for an inspired spark, something of the whimsical and unanticipated, an imaginative ploy that would also be advantageous. But all he could come up with was the obviousness of his own blackness, and the fact the hairless ones would not be expecting a black leopard. That dread deadline of noonday, when the sun covers the jungle completely in its light, hung like a curse. In exasperation with his inability to conjure up anything more original than just his coat colour, the panther was on the verge of slinking off into the maze of vegetation - falling without a break all the way down to the lower slopes - when, through a flurry of wing flaps, a call he thought he'd never hear again drilled like a thunderbolt into his scramble of thoughts.

The instant a familiar croak cut the air, the panther's face brightened with that radiant glow of illumination only serendipitous discovery brings:

"Umbulala - I've stayed to aid you!"

The whimsical and unanticipated had arrived in the form of a bird with a red tail, and a very special talent.

"The hairless ape is making a contraption…." the Grey parrot squawked breathlessly, settling on an overhead branch "that when tripped will set off the scorching wrath of a firestick. See how the hairless one keeps walking back and forth adjusting it - the idea is that a gorilla will trigger it. The reed leaning against the twig is the trick: it will bring Brother death to whoever unwittingly dislodges it!"

The big cat, his jaw dropping open in a conspiratorial grin, grunted softly up at the parrot for only her to hear:

"Little sister - fly to the tree nearest the one at the snare, and when I'm in position, let loose in that clever way of yours, in the tongue of hairless ape, a loud warning call of 'LEOPARD'!! But *only* when the moment is right."

She flew straight as a shooting star into the cover of trees. Slipping off the rock slab after her, the panther snorted in amazed admiration to himself, trying to imagine a Go-away bird responding so eagerly and with such celerity, and couldn't. It would instead hop about demanding endless explanations, before expanding on any number of pointless alternatives. Just then admiration began to dissolve into the kind of misgivings that can only be sent to test resolve. Umbulala suddenly began to wonder if the parrot would remember what to do; what, for instance, would she see as the 'right moment'; did she even know their sound for leopard!? As dread doubt began to spin its mischief, the big cat quickened his pace to match his galloping thoughts. But the precept of letting wisdom be master hadn't been lost; no sooner had unfounded misgivings about the parrot arisen, then unconscious inner prudence began to work to dismiss them from mind. *Be gone Brother error,* the panther's thoughts sizzled, and his pace slackened in rhythm with his calming senses.

Reaching the general area he'd ear-marked from the parapet, Umbulala slipped deeper into the undergrowth just about where he guessed the hairless apes to be, and steadily closed in. The distance between dropped away with every pawfall until, irrevocably, the one sensory medium he could always rely on brought an odour on the wind that offered little doubt. There was no denying that unpleasant presence: he had reached the gully clearing with the hairless ape and the snare - and, by now, the Grey parrot in her role as sentinel. There was but one other undeniable sign of something being out-of-place. Silence, that unfailing warning call the wild sends out as reliably as the rising of the moon, had fallen - complete and incontestable - like some predestined marker of what was to unfold. Anonymous mid a fall of foliage, the Grey was attentively watching the hairless ape put the finishing touches to the snare. Peeping from under cover, her neat, alert head was bobbing inquisitively from side to side in that matchless way of parrots. She was perfectly placed to monitor the approach of the panther, now but a buffalo space behind the hairless ape whose back, unfortunately for the hairless ape, was firmly turned to the advancing cat. Like lightning striking without warning the stillness was torn asunder by a cry so all-embracing, it nearly startled the intent panther out of his skin:

"Leopard! Leopard!! A *Leop-aaaarddd!*"

The jungle erupted with the frenetic activity of unseen animals suddenly deprived of their serenity. The usual blur of birds and small animals spurted from cover in all directions. Of more substantial shapes Umbulala was conscious of were the red flashes of a duiker, diving into the bordering density of undergrowth, and a Forest buffalo jerking in characteristic galumphing motion the opposite way. It was in the fleeting instant between the two that the hairless ape, in a reflex all animals answer to in moments of alarm, spun round to face the fearsome spectre of a snarling, growling panther, fangs seemingly dripping menace. Here was every hallucinatory chimaera rolled into one, monstrous, black cat with the magic of conjuring up voices from nowhere! The disorientated hairless ape instinctively spun away, vainly casting around for help, a weapon, a way out. But Brother error was skipping right alongside. In the haste of the moment the trap's crucial triggering device - the reed of grass on which so much attention had been laboured - was kicked away.

This simple act set in train a fatal chain reaction. Knocked aside, the sapling was immediately sprung, releasing the operating mechanism of the gun-trap to fire off both barrels in one deadly flash of force. The solid shot exploded with a loud report - *bb-bb-BOOMMMM* - as lead balls the size of quail eggs blasted into the hairless one's chest. The ferocity of such an impact on flesh and bone must be seen to be believed: at the sheer pummelling punch of it the hairless ape was spun violently round and propelled backward by at least a body length….till just a paw touch away. But Umbulala remained rigid as rock seared to the spot, eyes riveted on a carcass contorting and twisting in terrible spasms until death came, and collected. A gaping bloodied hole in the back gave every impression of an elephant having thrust a tusk into it; and a vaguely numbed Umbulala spat under his breath about how here was one hairless ape who'd have known something of how the silverback, and others, had died: agonisingly.

At the now rapid approach of the other hairless ape in reaction to the shots and cries, a frantic alert rang out from the ever-vigilant Grey parrot; again in disarming imitation of the hairless apes, but in this instance as an urgent, coded alarm to draw the panther's attention to impending danger:

"Leopard leopard! AAGGHH - it's a LEOPARD!!"

It had the desired effect. At the moment of the parrot's cry, Umbulala turned in

the direction intended - just as the poacher arrived in the cat's sightline. The very air seemed to hang suspended as he faced down a new adversary: this one openly armed. Swiftly drawing his paws up under him, the panther readied himself for attack. This new arrival would

have been prepared to rendezvous with a leopard, that's for certain; but not, it must be presumed, a leopard of the type about to be confronted head on. In spite of a degree of breathlessness and a shocked look of surprise, the hairless ape raised what Umbulala recognised as a deadly 'firestick'. Narrowing one eye along its blue-black barrel, lining up the front sight with the niche of the back sight and levelling both until aimed between the panther's eyes, a quivering but ready finger moved to squeeze the trigger. Umbulala was but a sunbird's wingbeat from hurling himself into a kill or be killed leap. He wasn't given the chance.

A terrible, high-pitched, screeching roar like nothing Umbulala had ever heard - for intensity, pitch and violence of tone one of the most explosive in nature - erupted from a bank of vegetation behind the hairless ape. A heartbeat later the foliage was ripped aside as two, massive furred arms burst through. In one downward swipe the powerful limb of a gorilla, its hand open - not clenched as might be expected - lashed lengthways down the hairless ape in one glancing blow. Thick solid fingers, with nails to match, slashed with an ease any predator would envy, propelling the poacher a zebra's length away. In a single flaying motion cloth and skin were sliced open, and raw flesh laid bare from chest to lower thigh.

Landing headfirst against a slab of rock, the sickening sound of bone breaking spoke volumes. As the skull cracked open readily as a newborn chick breaks through eggshell, the body momentarily froze - before slumping motionless into an embrace of ferns, blood trickling tellingly from between the still quivering lips. Umbulala was stunned at how frail the hairless ape was in the absence of fur, hide or muscle that could take a clout with any degree of force behind it. How a form so fragile could be so feared flabbergasted him - and with the realisation came avowal, as in the final unravelling of a great intrigue. Beyond the trappings of weapons, snares and numbers there was nothing; nothing beyond the ruthless determination to overpower and control, and the grit that goes with it.

A massive silverback burst into the open. Rising up on his hind legs with his head and torso hunched menacingly forward, the gorilla proceeded to beat a rapid, resonating tattoo on his chest with his great gauntlets of hands slightly cupped. Like a hefty stick alternately striking a hollow tree trunk, it resounded round the gully thence on through the forest seemingly - the cat wouldn't have been surprised to learn - forever. With intervals of hoots growing faster and louder, the silverback then entered into a hair-raising display terrifying to all, except maybe other gorillas. Running in quick, bipedal sideways bursts, with one shoulder intimidatingly in front of the other, the bull thrashed at the vegetation with ferocious overhand swipes, tearing at branches, tossing them about, throwing a leg in the air, before rounding off with a definitive, thudding thump of the ground with the palm of a great hand.

Watching all this assiduously - critical, should the huge beast turn his attention on him - Umbulala, rather than flee, had sunk instinctively into an attacking crouch. Leopards, after all, have killed gorillas, silverbacks included, *and* in these very mountains, Brother wind had diplomatically let slip. In fact outside of hairless apes, leopards are a gorilla's only real threat. Be that as it may, it didn't take much for Umbulala's mind to empty of any illusions, yet alone optimism, as the silverback veered threateningly closer, yellow fangs bared. Dropped squarely on all fours the silverback stood rigidly awhile staring fixedly at nothing in particular, suddenly lunged forward, then as abruptly again stopped. Although only a bluff, intense eyes glowering from under the huge domed brow characteristic of the heavily furred mountain gorilla, set above a strapping frame of colossal, thickset shoulders and brawny arms - the combined power of which can't be surpassed - makes for an awesome vision of might that can disarm even the most stout-hearted!

Umbulala was rooted to the spot. Yet he was enough of the uncompromising observer to still allow himself to be, not so much overawed, but intrigued by the gorilla's outward ferocity, and how it didn't appear to be driven by any inborn aggression.   The innate spirit of the hunter which imbues the leopard, the jungle's consummate predator, was not this beast's motivating force.   This great ape was reacting protectively to what it perceived as a territorial threat to itself and its family group; no more, no less.   Though looking and sounding mind-numbingly savage, killer instinct - that do-or-die capacity to drive a kill all the way - was lacking.   In place was the need to fend off a challenge with bluff or, if unavoidable, physical contact meant as nothing more than a deflective swipe; only the inescapable fact of the gorilla's brute strength turning it to something more than a shove out of the way.

No indeed.   From the panther's standpoint this great ape was no strategist, with a prerequisite predatory appetite for hunting that marks the leopard; in fact no desire in general to kill, as much as repel; killing being what happens by default, rather than calculated design.   The gorilla barked unthreateningly, an inflective *uh-uh-u* call infused with wonder:

> "The sunbird claimed Mother nature had summoned the aid of a panther to counter the hairless ones - but *what* need had we for a black leopard to help rid the jungle of these treacherous apes; now I know! Your strategy so compromised them,

there was no escape.   Go now, to your own domain, and live long!   You will not be forgotten, Umbulala."

The panther grunted softly back in return:

"And you, mighty ape, made a fine ally at such close quarters…..."

and a terrifyingly daunting one too might well have followed in silent afterthought.

The big silverback hovered a moment, eyes casting thoughtfully about. Then holding his splendid body straight-backed and erect - the powerful, thickly furred arms bent outward to make them appear even more impressive than they already were - the big gorilla began to knuckle-walk away in a rigid, sideways strut. Carefully watching the panther out of the corner of his eye, the steps were deliberately short and abrupt, so to show off in profile his physique to its full magnificence. Presently, silver-saddled and gleaming in his blue-black coat, the gorilla melded back into the cover of jungle.

The atmosphere tingled with the immensity of it all. Umbulala slowly checked around. The Grey parrot had long gone, but the big cat had no desire to rush. He was too spellbound with elation; the kind one feels after coming through a gruelling ordeal, and he savoured the freedom of the feeling without giving thought to however long it would enrapture him. He dozed a bit, in between musing deeply on all that had just passed…..and what had passed before that.

When at last his whirling senses had settled again into an even tempo, the big panther roused himself. He stretched out - one long, sinuous, galluptious stretch - before letting his muscles relax back in the way one does when giving vent to a long held sigh; and on looking up saw a familiar red-tailed bird, very distinctive and very determined in her flight, darting overhead, on toward the sunset.

"Farewell hunter of the night......" the Grey parrot called down, "may Mother nature be with you. Now I follow the setting sun to find my kin."

The panther raised himself up onto his paws, and with his ebony head held high, unashamedly roared back in that sawing cough of leopard for all to hear:

"May you find your kinfolk little Sister, and may Mother nature keep you and yours safe from the grasping grip of hairless apes. I wish you many young ones!" and he tracked her flight all the way until it was one with the sky.

Dropping his gaze, the big cat checked the surrounding gully clearing: all was still, so infinitely still - the motionless hairless apes, the trace left behind of the departed silverback. It was time to take his leave of this realm of the Mountain gorilla.

Lighter of mind and heart, an almost carefree swagger began to invest Umbulala's gait again. As he made away, he couldn't resist a satisfied snort to himself on now that it was over and done, there'd be no more worries about hairless apes. All at once, with that roughshod indifference fate treats our most sublime of high points, the panther found himself halting in his tracks. A breeze blowing with a peculiar urgency around an imposing stand of bamboo was commanding his attention, and on lifting his head to scent the air, its hollow stems began to sing a solemn lament fit to smart his senses:

"Would that it could be so, hunter of the night" it seemed to sigh, "but already they've penetrated the land of hot sand where there is no water; frozen wastelands too, where rain falls as ice, whiting out the earth in layers so deep, not even a grassy sprig reaches for the light; places so desolate no plants to speak of grow."

As the sombre litany whined on, the panther's heady carefreeness steadily receded to levels more conducive to survival.

"Here, by contrast, in the heart of the tropical jungle there's life in abundance; so here, too, more and more will come….."

the wind blew a chill chastener so that nothing should be left forgotten,

"not just for its creatures - but for its trees and its plants, its rocks....for the very ground itself."

And somehow, deep in his gut, the panther knew it all to be true, for hadn't others hinted as much?

Thus with a racing heart and a quickening pace he hastened away down the slopes - down and down, far from the bamboo groves and the misty glades; down by the lake with the waving papyrus; down over the foothills of Coral trees ablaze in scarlet-brush flowers; down along wooded riverbanks dotted with palms and the fiery bursts of Flame of the Forest trees; on and on, beyond the spreading tracts of mighty Ironwoods and Mahoganys - on back to the accustomed cadence of his own, far-gone territory.

Hyaena

WHERE ONLY THE STARS CAN SEE ME

*The past, like a loyal shadow, gently
guides the present on to the future*

The further one moves into true Mopane forest there's an increase in game obvious to the eye. Handsome groves of these butterfly-leafed trees, and a ground cover of finer, sweeter grasses, draw a rich mix of animals, from elephants and giraffes, strapping kudu, sable and roan, to smaller browsers and grazers alike. It was morning on the fringes of *miombo* woodland dominated by Musasa trees - awash in season in a an unforgettable flush of orange-gold and bronze - where it slowly melds to open stands of tall Mopane. The *wet* was in full flourish, and the sunwashed, blue-skied exuberance of fresh green everywhere the panther looked was entrancing. In this heady rush of first growth, running the gamut of verdurous tones in every leaf that glints in the sunshine, there's a lightness, a luminescence behind every spray of foliage and blade of grass that veritably glows. It's an ethereal translucence conspicuously missing in the denser, never-ending greenness of the equatorial rainforests.

Umbulala was back in the jungle country bordering his home range, and on a whim was taking an unhurried diversion into nostalgia through a remote chunk of his mother's territory where it ran adjacent to his own. Memories of the area were wistful ones, given its proximity to where Sibindi had been slain by hairless apes. Many a sunrise had come and gone since his sojourn in the

WHERE ONLY THE STARS CAN SEE ME

domain of the mountain gorillas, where he'd put the hairless ones to rout, adding just a little to the legend in the process. Yet in spite of the chastening predictions that had darkened his leave-taking, the elation which he'd felt at the end of that fraught foray - when against the odds he'd set the record straight for others like Sibindi - was with him still, cocooning him in a protecting veil against the malicious onslaught of memory. Hence, on balance, it was a cat comfortable within himself taking the long trek back through many changing vistas; a leisurely stroke more and more imbuing every step the closer he came to familiar hunting grounds.

He dozed mid a perfumed burst of yellow blossoms at the heart of a Bloodwood tree, so dubbed for the copious red sap its thick bark exudes when slashed. Stashed higher up the tree's branches under its flat crown was the partly consumed carcass of an impala. Umbulala stirred; he hadn't been asleep, just resting mind and body in that therapeutic, *dolce far niente* way of cats. Without shifting position by a trace noticeable to an onlooker, he cast a veiled glimpse round through half-closed eyes. Dawn had come and gone, the midmorning sun shooting piercing rays through the foliage, as if picking out nesting spots for small miracles to roost: a bird, wiping its beak on a patch of wood, and leaving behind a seed to attach itself and sprout a leaf; a clinging epiphyte taking hold; a moth laying an egg. Umbulala never ceased to delight in how, in these fractured streams of light, one could see sunbeams dance; a phenomenon with no practical purpose he could readily think of, and as such could only be intended by nature for the enjoyment of those with a shared empathy.

The big cat's face was barely visible, tucked away mid a mass of black fur in the well of shadow shrouding the bosom of the tree. The first sign of life was when a single ear pricked up. Appearing like a miniature glossy starling glinting in a shaft of sunlight, it cupped and turned to locate the source of a melodious *hoop-hoop-oo-hoophoooo* that had been penetrating his repose, gently nudging his senses to attention. The call floated up from beyond a rambling scramble of shrubbery prettily garlanded in creepers of morning glories, white trumpet flowers ablaze in the sun. In an unmistakable russet-orange flash, a dashing hoopoe - wings slickly barred in black and white - was probing the ground with a long bill, the elegant swept-back head bobbing busily. With a conspicuously regal crest it raises now and then into a spectacular swirl as it moves about feeding, the terrestrial hoopoe is a stirring sight, and a dreamy Umbulala couldn't help thinking of it as a winged blossom; even a 'feathered' butterfly, which oddly enough, in its style of flight, a hoopoe is not unlike.

Attention-grabbing as it was, right now Umbulala was aware of something more compelling than Brother hoopoe; something beyond the lilting tremolo of a Woodland kingfisher, or the pink and white lilies scattering the vlei where an

alluring plethora of life was coming and going; a commanding presence with an disarming pull in the vicinity of a nearby kopje.   Heaven for an enchantment of klipspringers and rock rabbits alike, the stony, crenellated hill of humps of granite and rounded boulders, piled on top of each other, was also notable for a radiance of Flame lilies sparkling among the shrubs crowding its lower rockery, their delicate red-gold beauty - curiously plain yellow at cooler altitudes   -   belied by the plants being poisonous if eaten. And something 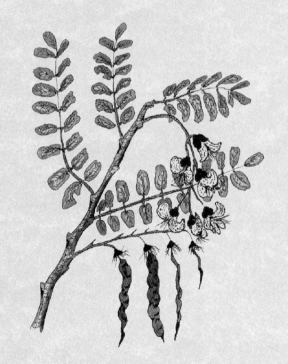 else. A familiar call crooned from the direction of the kopje:

"Is this the cub who vowed never to return here - this panther too big to heed warnings not to tangle with hairless apes?"

UMBULALA

As the greeting cough of leopard cut like an icicle through the torpid throb of the rising heat of morning, Umbulala flung his head to attention, every hair of his hide coming alive, sensory organs on full alert, ears cupped to catch every nuance of sound and movement. Peering down, wide eyes dancing in cublike anticipation, the panther's sharp gaze raced to pinpoint the hunter in the tracery of greenery. Then he sighted it, through a gap no bigger than a ground squirrel's head - a snatched peek of a spotted hide. The panther trilled back in eager acknowledgement, his eyes softening to the warm gold of the leopard at play:

"Ingwe! It has been too many moons - how goes it with you mother?"

At that the foliage parted, and an ageing leopardess emerged into the open, strolling with slow dignity to the tree. The panther was quick to notice the touch of fragility about her; a fragility not there when their ways last converged. But though she was thin, her hygiene hadn't slipped. Her coat was as rich and finely groomed as ever. Yet he couldn't deny what his eyes were seeing: Inqwe, mighty hunter and wise teacher of his cubhood was no longer the cat he had known and cherished. With effort she climbed the tree. Moving toward the panther, now up on his haunches and making room for her, Ingwe rubbed her head against his, grunting in a low, familiar tone:

"The sight of you thrills me, but unnerves me too; tales of your adventures are legion, and leave me as much proud, as fearful for your safety...." she purred, "though I'm wise enough to know many are embellished to suit the teller. It so pleases me our paths have crossed - I was about to seek you out."

The panther in turn rubbed his head along her neck:

"Then Mother nature has smiled on us both. So what's with you Ingwe?" an enquiring purr rumbled softly up from the black cat, "I sense all is not well."

Digging in her claws she began to drag them methodically down the fissured wood of the branch, blood-red runnels oozing up in their wake to plot tell-tale tracks along the blackened bark. As if purified by this most habitual act in the grooming rite, Ingwe relaxed. She slowly cast a glance round, then, shaking her coat into place, fell into a snaking stretch along the limb. Clasping her eyes on the now legendary panther before her - cub of hers, sight of whom was balm for her heart and spirit - Ingwe, decorum regained, yielded to the luxury of the heartfelt purr, long repressed, and now released to freely well up from within:

"I seek a favour but fear you may not take me seriously; yet my wish is sincere, and so small. Brother death has shadowed me all rainy season" she intoned with quiet resolve "and of late so close: watching, waiting - not jeering nor barracking - just waiting. I fear the hyaena, and have no wish to be scraps for those slavering scavengers. Let me cross your territory to the low escarpment and its caves, there to see out my days away from the marauding throng, safe from their sneering gaze and contemptuous ways."

Umbulala nudged her with affection, grunting a gentle rebuke:

"You are but skin and bone and couldn't yet make the climb. Here now, eat your fill...." he motioned to the remains of the carcass "then come hunt with me; when the moon has circled in full, you've regained some weight and your stamina has revived - all in all, revitalised - together we'll make that climb; but not to the caves of your imagining." No, much further: to the rock shelters of the far-gone highlands whence he'd just returned. "To the white peaks that brush the moon where hyaenas and their ilk will never touch you. This I can promise; as for Brother death, only Mother nature can help you there."

Ingwe's whole bearing and mien lightened. Manoeuvring closer the carcass, she wiggled into a position from which she could eat comfortably. The leopardess began to pick at it, tentatively at first. Then in almost sheer abandon she began to eat with unrestrained relish, as if she'd suddenly discovered a terrible hunger she'd been too proud to reveal; a relish heightened by the rare piquancy of not having had to make the kill herself. It was many, many moons back that was so; indeed, a lifetime past when she herself was but a cub. Eventually lifting her head, Ingwe purled in unadulterated contentment - impala hadn't tasted so good in a stream of seasons, and already she felt it fuelling her for the task ahead. Just then the decidedly unwelcome, in the guise of a vulture swooping down to land in a tree opposite, intruded on the leopards' shared reverie. Unwelcome - because it was a Lappet-faced vulture, classic carrion bird of ill-omen.

It's unusual for a vulture to come close to leopard, unless the cat is on a kill too large to take up a tree; even then it'll keep at a safe distance. Hence the presence nearby of the bird didn't go unremarked. Huge vultures of the archetypal fleshy head, face and neck on which raw-pink skin, pinched and pitted - and hanging in folds in places - sits unsavourily on an ill-tempered countenance, Lappets are loners with a cheerless demeanour even other vultures give way to! Spreading large, black-brown wings ominously wide - as if laying claim to a cadaver - the Lappet stretched out a heavy, hooked beak. From under a hooded brow, scowling eyes sought for the spotted cat. Initially finding it difficult focusing at short range, a scornful leer soon fell on Ingwe - and with it a mordant yelp cut the air:

"I've been eyeing you all season, old one: why bother with scraps from your cub - you're no longer fit for the jungle. We need food for our own, and your hanging on to life is denying us that right!"

Ingwe was stung by the vulture's sniping reproach; yet she gave nothing out, not the merest hint. Umbulala glared briefly at the blathering bird with the disdain he reserved for vultures, marabou storks and their ilk, considering them nothing more than scruffy vagabonds of the air. Treating it to a perfunctory, albeit smouldering glance, he flicked his gaze back to Ingwe. Searching, quizzing, almost daring her to show a trace of unease he focused on his mother's face - staring, unmoved, into space - until she finally relented under the black leopard's incisive stare:

"It's a topsy-turvy world the jungle: once that feathered degenerate and the rest of the horde wouldn't have come within range of me; now....." Ingwe growled softly "they snap at my heels, not for my leftovers, but for my body, my very own flesh and bones. I know...." she sighed resignedly, "it keeps the jungle healthy; even so, I have no wish to demean this leopard that is Ingwe by bending to them."

She looked Umbulala full in the face and saw not scorn, only warmth and kinship; he, by turn, acknowledged the meaning in her look and purred a reassurance:

"It is all in the game of life - as Brother wind would have it, don't lose sight of your desires; and while we can see to it you don't end up fodder for such as these, we can't beat Brother death when on our trail at the chosen moment. It would be better to move during the day, and to rest at night."

Ingwe nodded in ready compliance, then turned back to feed as if the vulture had never existed.

The two leopards went on to hunt together over many dawns and sunsets, with Ingwe recovering a sizeable proportion of her weight; and while still a little slower than in her prime, much of her former vigour. Now she was able to sleep too; and sleep more content than she had in a long while. At last, on a day capped by a sky emblazoned blue from horizon to horizon, the two set off side by side. The panther, who dwarfed Ingwe, eased his rate, adjusting his stride so not to outpace his mother, moving with a slightly laboured gait. The going would be strenuous for the older cat, and this bore heavily on him as he looked away into the distance - away in his mind's eye beyond gorilla country to where the Mountains of the Moon would be resolutely brushing the clouds; where, too, snow-shrouded peaks would be melding, as ever, to myriad creeks rushing their sustenance down to the thirsty lowlands. Umbulala adjured Ingwe not to be ashamed to stop and rest - there was no race, and every day together would be a joy to savour; it was all they had. And thus did the sentiments of the one, echo precisely those of the other.

So on they roamed - under clear, cloudless skies, over hills and ridges, along gullies and soggy vleis, through meandering tracts of rolling bush, much of it luxuriant forest-like woodland, the rest gnarled and stunted. After journeying some distance, an inviting waterhole watched over by a rambling grove of Strangler Fig trees, beckoned a shady diversion. The leopards plopped down on a cooling, grassy sward across which a mating pair of Paradise flycatchers had declared full aerial sovereignty. A spectacle of glossy blue-green and chestnut - the trailing tail plumes of the cock gracefully sweeping the air in flight - they were boldly going about domestic duties, showily darting between the water and the Figs, and as such difficult to ignore. With clearly a brood in the tree cover to feed, the flycatchers showed little interest in the cats. Even before the upbringing of their chicks begins, Paradise flycatchers conscientiously share the task of incubating the eggs. Hence here was a doting pair too involved flitting to and fro in their characteristic undulating flight gathering food for nestlings to be much bothered by leopards! Once replete with a beakful of the insects they catch on the wing, each would return again and again to the chicks in a nest formed among the fig leaves; a dainty, cupped artifice of spiderwebs and moss delicately wrought together.

Eventually duty called for Ingwe too; stepping from the shadows, she took a leisurely stroll to the water. In seeming disregard to the flycatchers and other birds picking them off, clouds of tiny flying insects whirled about in spirals above it. Reaching the pool edge, Ingwe had just begun to lap away unhurriedly when, out of her sightline, two hyaena broke cover. With the obvious aim of ambushing the aged leopardess while she was in the open with her back turned, they lolloped toward her. But Ingwe's reflexes had dulled little. Instinctively alerted to an unwelcome presence behind her, it was first the rallying giggle - a dead giveaway which might be acceptable on the scavenge, but not wise when bushwhacking a big cat - followed by an overpowering whiff of hyaena that left little doubt.

The leopardess span round spitting and snarling to face down the challenge head on; she'd lost none of her fire, and despite her reduced physical condition those reflexes were still rapier sharp. Momentarily wrong-footed by Inqwe's rapid response, more of the same was about to be unleashed from the opposite direction. The hyaenas had missed the black shape lounging to the rear, concealed in the deep shadows cast by the columnar trunks, aerial roots and spreading crowns of the Fig trees - until it leapt at them from behind. The panther went straight for the nape of the neck of the dominant hyaena. With a wrenching flick of his head, he snapped her spine, tossing her aside like a disreputable bundle. Ingwe was in mid-charge at the remaining, smaller hyaena. The dog swung round to flee; as it did it ran headlong into the panther - and another hyaena became food for its kind, dispatched in a blurred surge of speed and indignation. That leopards don't much care for hyaenas is sacred writ. It's a distaste only surpassed by the utter contempt that infuses the treatment lions reserve for hyaenas, whenever the chance arises.

"I'm not sure you even needed my help, little Mother; so much like a cub did I feel next to such a master hunter...."

Umbulala crooned as they rested back in the soothing shade of the Fig trees, mutually grooming away the toils of the fray. Sustenance for the soul is the praise that's quietly given. Ingwe had a clearer slant on it: while there was no questioning the will of the spirit and her unwavering response to the call, the

input of the panther had been the pivot on which it had turned, without which the outcome would otherwise have been - if not detrimental - at least different.

"Before a paw was raised you were the fire fanning my fearlessness...." with every hair on her back still raised Ingwe coughed softly in response, a modest note of triumph, not least a touch of surprise, evident mid the relief,

"even putting to rout the grim force that's been shadowing me - as nowhere did I see Brother death."

After the encounter at the waterhole the leopards were to cover a vastness of bushland and jungle, far from hyaenas and their dread ilk. And rather than the sombre pilgrimage it could so readily have been, it was a voyage neither wished nor wanted to rush, delighting in each other's company, complete in their final togetherness. Past the first of the great lakes, and on into the steamy heart of the evergreen rainforests they roved, over many sunrises, along increasingly untrodden trails, exploring, hunting, eating together like companions sharing an unending adventure, savouring every moment. They wandered on to where the jungle begins to climb, first gradually, then sharply to the montane forests of the great rift escarpment. A geological marvel slicing like a gigantic furrow through earth's surface, fractures and movement from long past, underground and above, have shaped all along its spectacular extent an unrivalled melange of mountains and glacier-clad crests, jagged ravines, forests and volcanoes.

A once drowned river valley dammed by lava flows, they ambled round a picturesque lake. In and out inlets and coves nestling between towering shafts of rock they slowly sauntered, thence on again through the vistas beyond to a majestic range of volcanoes soaring up to the clouds, guided there by the peaked summit of *Muhavura* 'who shows the way'. And as they trekked on together from sunrise to sunset, Ingwe took it all in her stride, rambling along rolling slopes, lingering in fecund gorilla tracts not long ago trod by Umbulala; stepping lightly through her wilderness world. Drinking in every delight and discovery along the way, their passage took them down again; through near impenetrable forest and along rushing rivers, on into welcoming woodlands and grassy spaces, round waterfalls and reed-clad swamps - on to the foothills of the Mountains of the Moon. It was to be from here, from this rich outlier of vegetation, that Ingwe and Umbulala would eventually set off on their last climb together, up to the rock-shelters and crags above the snowline where no hyaenas venture, no scavengers alight.

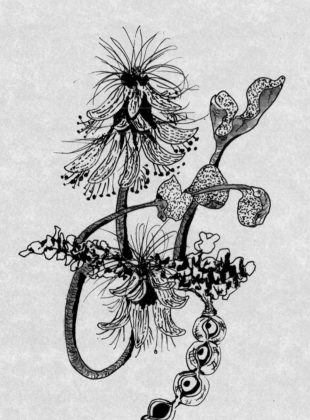

First fate decreed they should loiter awhile mid the palm groves and arbours of flowering trees which splash pink and scarlet around its lower gradients; refreshing and recharging themselves before the long ascent up over bracken-covered slopes to the swathe of forest that wraps the mountains. Under a broken canopy, a meld of Stinkwood and Podo trees, shorter ferns and bananas, weave and string through a luxuriant understorey that winds all the way to the bamboo belt. Here the towering grass doesn't grow in any clearly defined belt. Instead, much of it occurs in intermittent stands dispersed through a maze of undergrowth dominated by flowering shrubs, blackberries and grassy glades flecked with everlastings and lilies. Representatives of those curious trees that had first beguiled Umbulala, then Ingwe, in gorilla tracts, hovered in splendid isolation, many hung with beard lichens, others rearing up from boggy patches like great, flowering spikes. It had all the look and feel of that unforgettable realm; but there were no gorillas in these mountains, jungle spaces unlike anywhere else.

Above the bamboo on the Mountains of the Moon the giant heath begins in earnest. For Ingwe this weird forest of heather trees - all furred and ruffed and hung with what looked for all the world like fleecy tails and wildebeest beards - was unlike anything in her experience. Far finer than what they'd encountered in the volcanoes, and in much greater density - its white, bell-shaped flowers now also pink - everything about it was in excess. On trunks up to several elephants tall, the trees were still draped in tresses of beard lichens; still padded in great, flocculent clumps of moss; the same moss, running from green to orange-gold, still clambered over the ground. Yet all on a scale so much greater.

In lavish stretches - where the heather was so closely packed its writhing branches virtually interlocked - the trees were festooned in gossamer leis of lichen; their stems and trunks so thickly clustered with bulbous pom-poms of moss there was barely a patch of wood visible; while not a spot of ground, not a stone, not an exposed, twisted root or fallen branch lay uncovered in a lustrous kaross of moss. To add to its otherworldliness, the whole forest - uncannily silent, its mantle of moss muffling even the sound of a tree limb swaying in the breeze - was bathed in a glow of sunlight that dispelled any mist. In fact sun and bright sky, not the customary rain nor ring of cloud that usually drifts up, were the constant companions of the two leopards. Such clear weather on these mountains is a rare privilege. It was as if their path on this special journey had been blessed; blessed by nature.

For some distance Ingwe and Umbulala had been tracking the swift-flowing course of a creek back upstream. Once they'd left the bamboo and nettles behind its clear waters wove alternately through heather forest and open meadows rich in herbage. It led past woodland on well drained slopes, celery and violets noteworthy among the undergrowth, and boggy valley bottoms of sedge rising up from the mire in tussocks which, decaying from their bases upwards, only the sure-footed hopping from clump to clump can negotiate without sinking up to their hocks. The creek, silvery and gurgling with pools dotted at turnings along its extent, was like all the watercourses hereabouts: crystal clear, being the run-off of glaciers either in retreat, or with hardly any forward movement. With no grinding action to speak of little in the way of detritus - that would otherwise give the streams a pearly consistency - comes down in the melt from their snows.

Leaving the heather behind, the creek began to climb through meadows cloaked in a silvery-leafed mantle that scrolled away under the unmatched beauty of everlastings in full bloom. Umbulala and Ingwe had entered the alpine zone, and as the pitch of the ground grew steeper with increasing altitude, the creek grew narrower. Eventually, no more than a stride across, it led up through a slim gap to the source of water that fed it. Nourished by the glaciers on the towering slopes around it, the lake lay cradled in a cirque in the very heart of the range. In weather still sparklingly clear its glassy surface danced in the sunlight, mirroring in breathtaking backdrop, under a curve of sky daubed in white billowy puffs of cloud, the cliffs and buttresses and ice-clad tops of the high peaks encircling it. The arresting shapes of Giant Groundsels scattering its verges completed a picture deserving of more than just a passing glance, and the cats skirted it in leisurely appraisal. Another entrancing scene, in a setting of tarns and frozen waterfalls, awaited - this one not so much breathtaking, as to leave one breathless.

After tripping nimbly through another patch of mud and sedge bogs, the leopards reached a broad pass in the range. Here a moorland of bizarre opulence opened out before them. In weather still fine and holding, it fell away clear and bright to the distant slopes beyond, to where the range rose on its final ascent, through glaciers and snowbridges, to the rim of an ice-plateau winking in the sun. Whatever its mood - washed in soft tropic sunlight or, as commonly prevails at these altitudes, cloud and mist - the afro-alpine zone is a world apart. That it marks the distributional limit for most animals seems oddly appropriate, for it unquestionably belongs to the bewitching flora that inhabits it, dominated by Giant Groundsels and Torch Lobelias, which in places flourish in such rampant growth and density, as to truly deserve the appellation 'forest'.

Among the most startling plant forms to be found anywhere, these high altitude versions surpassed any Umbulala and Ingwe had already seen: the chunky rosette heads of the Groundsels atop woody trunks taller than ever; statuesque Lobelias soaring straight and torch-like, tiny  blue blossoms on their flower spikes picked over in silvery hairs creating an effect strangely alluring. Ingwe, for whom the giant heather was impressive, was agog; even the ground cover bushes of everlastings were substantial enough to dwarf the leopards! Hence in this place of few animals - beyond moles, shaggy mountain rats and hyraxes, where even plants that had become familiar reached unaccustomed proportions - Umbulala was struck by a sight he'd never have envisaged being pleased to see again. Shimmering green shapes were darting around the Lobelias: it seemed an aeon back, but Scarlet-tufted malachites flitting in dazzling blurs about these graceful plants they play a part in pollinating, gave a continuity to it all that was curiously comforting. He had little doubt. Without the gorillas and the wisdom acquired on that sobering venture, what was now unfolding would be that much heavier.

Streaking down a great, towering shaft of rock beyond the moorland a shiny slither glistened silver in the sunlight. It was the tumbling path of a waterfall. From where the leopards looked across at it over the tops of the Groundsel and Lobelias it was clear and sparkling; only on nearing it did they notice the water was actually frozen; frozen like a single, great icicle stringing down the stony facade. It was just so with the swampy area of bog they found themselves emerging into. Here shallow, scattered puddles were covered in flaky layers of ice. Ingwe bent over one. Peering down into it, she sharply jerked her head back as if stung by something, blinking over and over at what it appeared to reflect: a fine cat in her prime. Ingwe focused again, and as it shivered into her own ageing image, she hissed in bemusement:

"Why, in this place without seasons, where life seems to stand still - this place of giant plants, where few birds sing and no animal noticeable to the eye roams - should Mother earth reflect what was?"

With the unerring certainty unpalatable truth brings, Inqwe spat into the wind. Her mind was as keen as when she was in her prime, yet her body had indeed moved on. And at last she understood - as the vulture had understood - how it was now right that her spirit should also move on.

As he stood by watching, helpless to know what to do, Umbulala was as much a muddle of confusion as despair; despair at how to ease his mother's pain, while not insulting her pride. And all at once he too knew what to do. Without fuss, just a warm, resounding mewl which said all that was needed, he tenderly nudged her, crooning gently as he did so:

"We've just a little way to go."

Ingwe softly nodded acknowledgement. Shaking herself vigorously by way of a freshener for the trek ahead she turned, then together with Umbulala moved off on the long, final ascent that would take her to beyond the snowline, and lasting sanctuary.

Passing into rocky country, the ground grew increasingly stony with every step. They soon left any vestige of vegetation behind, the last stragglers of Lobelias and Groundsels long petering out. Overhead, great wedges of exposed rock, polished black by the constant dampness, loomed out of the snow higher up the slopes, with beyond this the bare, mountainous expanse of glaciers, ice pinnacles and snow plateaux where nothing grows. Much of the rock they began clambering over was layered in lichen and moss - slippery in places, and thus demanding more vigilance the steeper the grade became. Mist began to appear too; but only in fleeting bursts according to the angle of the slopes, or however much the enclosing mountains crowded out the light. Otherwise the going was still bright and clear. The sun still smiled on the leopard pair; still immersed them in its reassuring beat.

With Inqwe leading the way, a wide ledge opened out before them, winding up the slopes to where two abutments at some stage passed had fused together. A ridge topped by a capacious shelf had formed; to the back of it a cave recessed deeply into the mountainside to form a shelter, tucked neatly in under the brow of a brooding overhang of stone so deep, its crest protruded from the topmost ramparts of the rockface sweeping imperiously up overhead below a hanging glacier. Here Ingwe halted. The view out from the ridge could only be as fate ordained. Free of cloud or mist or any obstruction, it looked clear away across a swell of sky, down over gullies and vales to the distant plains of the lowlands.

Ingwe lingered, staring long and hard into the unflagging distance, then back over everything between; drawing deeply on the whole, breathless pageant so not to lose sight nor sound of a minutia of it. Contenting herself with being able to see the valley of her birth only in imagination, her gaze tripped wistfully over the scene, over that vast scope of sky and land, back down the intervening moons of memory to far-gone territorial haunts she would never trod again. Umbulala joined her. The last of the day's sunlight played warmly about the leopards. As the first blush of the setting sun began to edge the horizon, there they remained in rapt observation, mother and cub on one last, shared quest. An orange-gold slowly seeped across the far plains; and as it sedately waltzed and sashayed up the lower valleys, the lengthening shadows of the retreating day began to stroke and finger the slopes and the rock around them in timely chorus.

Despite the cave being bigger inside than had been the impression from outside, to Umbulala's undeclared relief its only opening was located away from the prevailing winds. Thus, with just one entrance and the drop of the overhang out front acting as an effective buffer against the weather, it was relatively snug and protected. It had been a long hike for both cats; one great, thrilling adventure that had led them across a magnitude of jungle; in and out its many moods; through the never-ending marvel of its open-ended hugeness and capacity for surprise. All of a sudden the immensity of the endeavour began to tell, and at last, here in the sanctity of the high mountains they had set out to conquer, Umbulala and Ingwe began to unwind. Making the most of the remnants of sun flitting in through the opening, Ingwe stretched like a honied ooze into the rays, wallowing in their seductive warmth. Umbulala spread himself some way forward of Ingwe, a little way to the side of the cave opening, tucking his generous paws under him, thick fur puffed up to hold in as much body heat as possible.

It was going to be a chill night; so much better, then, to be in the cosier confines of a rock-shelter than outside it. Once the sun drops below the horizon and darkness descends, the cold on these mountains grips like an eagle's talons. Air from the upper snows scoots down the slopes, generating strong winds; fluffs of cumulus cloud that hug the peaks by day vanish, leaving a sky wondrously clear, with any remaining warmth rapidly dissipating with it. As temperatures plummet the night freeze is so severe the surface of glaciers, softened to a slush in the high altitude sun of the day, are frozen again before long. For all this the sight, when revealed, of snow-capped crests lit by a tropic moon under a sky unmatched - outside the equatorial mountains - for the size and brightness of its stars is worth any temporary discomfort.

Ingwe was heartened Umbulala was with her. It showed in her manner and mien as she faced out past him through the cave entrance on the sunset-dappled scene beyond; proud and erect and sphinx-like, her contentment replete with Umbulala close by. For his part the panther couldn't help but notice how pleasurably her primrose eyes sparkled and danced, as if she were in the first flush of youth, death furthest from mind. Anticipating his welter of thought, Ingwe purred from the heart of a cat at peace:

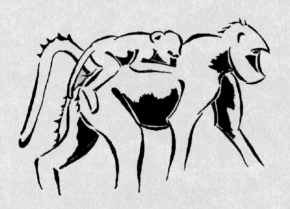

"I see the wider jungle and my distant valley spread before me, and it pleasures my heart that a cub of mine could lead me safely up through all its hazards to this far place where the Mountains touch the Moon.....and only the stars can see me."

The panther eased his body and limbs into a more relaxed pose while continuing to glance aside at Ingwe, musing on what a fine sight she made - upright and ever watchful, front paws stretched before her, head held smartly up, ears cupped to catch every nuance. Remaining alert to all this, still taking in everything his senses would allow, it was the last the panther remembered. He was suddenly hit by an overwhelming desire to sleep. As if some command beyond his control had taken ahold of his will, he lazily curled round; no sooner had he done so, he was drawn deeper into slumber.

Ingwe's gaze had been wavering between the dying embers of sunset through the cave entrance, and the panther grappling silently with his unbearable desire to sleep. She watched bemusedly as his head would nod one moment, bolt back upright in a fierce jerk the next, then nod slowly forward again, as if pressured by some unseen force. Eventually, no fight left, the ebony head dropped softly to rest between his front and back legs. Meeting in the soft curve of his body, all that remained to complete this ritualistic act of the cat falling into sacred repose was for his long tail to twirl elegantly round and wrap him up in one cosy curve, so to seal out the cold and damp from his paws, jaws and undersides. *Fait accompli:* what nature intends, nature does.

With that the light outside the rock-shelter began to drop; drop quickly as it does in the jungle like a buzzard on its prey. Very soon after it had faded altogether - relegating Ingwe's treasured view to final memory - she watched rise in its place a moonlit sky streaked with stars; stars of such brightness the observer of such a hallowed sight can never feel alone. At some stage as she watched on - watched, for one last time, yet another dazzling display of nature's artistry - a shadow slipped imperceptibly past the sleeping panther, up to her side. There death touched her. Stretched out erect and upright, Ingwe rose instantly at its beckoning call; as she did her body stayed, rigid and still, fixed to the spot. As flesh remains, spirit departs. Halting beside the sleeping Umbulala, death was in no hurry to rush her as she looked down at him sleeping softly: as she gazed one last, lingering moment on the mighty panther she had borne. Then, with an upward tilt of her head, she strolled unburdened of care from the cave, out into the starlit night, never to tread earthbound trails again.

Umbulala slept on until night melded to dawn. Not until the first streams of sunlight ebbing through the cave entrance began to flitter about him did he wake. He had never slept so long; not all the way through from dusk, except when injured. He dreamily wondered about this - before summarily dismissing it from mind as he recalled where he was, and why. Turning a drowsy glance on his mother he piped a greeting:

"Are you well Ingwe?"

The returning silence was galvanizing, searing his waiting senses through. He focused on every part of her. She was, as he remembered before sleep had ambushed his reason, perfect in every way. Except her eyes: their sparkle had fled - there was no dance left in them. Umbulala sprang up and hastened over to the outstretched figure. She was still as stone. The tell-tale stiffening of the body that follows death had set in. But there was an added factor:  with every vestige of blood-heat having long deserted her body at this altitude, she was virtually frozen in place, as if entombed in an invisible shroud of ice.

Umbulala nudged her affectionately in that way of cats the jungle over. But long before going through the motions truth had dawned. He nuzzled her neck and chest over and over, drawing deeply on the scent of her as if wanting, needing, to indelibly stamp every trace of her on himself, albeit knowing all the while he would never, could never forget her. His mind was a broiling turmoil of angst: remorse for not being at her side the moment it happened; puzzlement at how Brother death had just slipped by unnoticed; guilt, in spite of what his head knew, at not holding death at bay; lastly, *ne plus ultra* - anguish at the finality of it all:

"Now she rests looking out over her jungle, the stars and moon her companions.....and no more need of me."

Pulling away, he turned - then strode purposefully to the entrance of the cave, not looking back. He didn't need to: Ingwe's image was forever etched in memory. As for those terms of acceptance he'd thrashed out between his head and his heart, they had only a tenuous hold. Unable to hold back, Umbulala snarled bitterly at the silent rock about him in a spontaneous protest at how, in not repelling Brother death, he had surely failed her. A heartbeat later he thought he heard breezing round the ramparts of this, her final resting place, her eternal lair - as much to assuage his ache of doubt, perhaps, as to reassure - a murmuring sigh: *no little Brother, not this time.*

Umbulala walked from the cave into the shining light of morning. The early frost was already evaporating in the clear, alpine sunshine, and the panther's sumptuous coat glinted bronze in its radiance. As he stood there, imbibing the crisp air of a fresh day, ruminating on what had passed, willing his malaise away, his gaze fell on the Alpine swifts swerving away from their night roosts. Gaping in appreciative reverence at these svelte, slick birds sleekly skimming the air - soaring one moment, swooping off the next to favoured feeding grounds lower down the mountain slopes - his anguish was dispelled in one uplifting, rejuvenating flash of enlightenment. Svelte; slick; sleek; flying high. That was Ingwe in life. So now in death - unfettered spirit liberated from a worn and tired shell.....flying free.

With that too, Umbulala, and lighter of heart he turned to move away. As he did, the hidden spots of leopard beneath the burnished hide of panther winked knowingly in the glow of morn. Perhaps Ingwe walked with him still.

Leopard

SELECTED BIBLIOGRAPHY

Melanistic variants of *Panthera pardus* more associated with Asia, the list references panthers in Africa, records of leopard behaviour, and other observations and research relevant to the text; appended are works published after this book was completed in 2000 that conjoin or corroborate in one way or another what is written herein.

Bailey, T.N. The African Leopard: Ecology & Behavior of a Solitary Felid. Columbia University Press 1993.

Baumgartel, W. The Gorilla Killer: *Wild Life and Sport,* Vol. 2, No. 2, pp.14-17, 1961.

Baumgartel, W. *Up Among the Mountain Gorillas.* New York: Hawthorn Books 1976.

Bere, R. *The Way To The Mountains of The Moon.* London: Arthur Barker Ltd. 1966.

Brown, L. *Africa.* London: Hamish Hamilton 1965.

Burbridge, B. *Gorilla.* New York: Century 1928.

Crossland, J.R./Parrish, J.M. *Wildlife Of Our World.* London & Glasgow: Collins Press 1934.

Dart, R.A. The Kisoro pattern of mountain gorilla preservation: *Current Anthropology,* 2 (5), pp. 510-11, 1961.

de Waal, F. *Good Natured: The Origins of Right and Wrong in Humans and Other Animals.* Harvard University Press 1999.

Dyer, A./Kuhn, B. *Classic African Animals: The Big Five.* New York: Winchester Press 1973.

Geddes, H. *Gorilla.* London: Melrose 1955.

Godsall Bottriell, L. *King Cheetah: The Story of The Quest.* Leiden: E.J. Brill 1987.

Godsall Bottriell, L. The cat that lost its spots: *The Guardian.* London: March 11 1993.

Godsall Bottriell, L. Knocking spots off the cheetah: *Geographical,* Vol. LXVI, No. 10, 1994.

Godsall Bottriell, L. *The Geographical Imperative:* Address to Royal Geographical Society. London: 1995.

Gould, S.J. *Dinosaur in a Haystack.* New York: Harmony Books 1996.

Guggisberg, C A W. *Wild Cats of the World.* David & Charles 1975.

Gunther, A. *Proceedings of the Zoological Society,* pp. 243-5. London: March 3 1885.

Gunther, A. *Proceedings of the Zoological Society,* pp. 203-5. London: April 6 1886.

Hall-Craggs, E. Skeleton of an adolescent gorilla: *Sth. African Journal of Science,* 57 (11), pp. 299-302, 1961.

Hall Craggs, E. Testis of *Gorilla gorilla beringei: Proc. Zoological Society,* 139: 511-515. London: 1962.

Herán, I., *Animal Coloration.* Prague: Hamlyn 1976.

Linden, E. *The Parrot's Lament.* London: Souvenir Press 1999.

Maberly, C.T. Astley. *Animals of East Africa.* Cape Town: Howard Timmins 1960.

Masson, J./McCarthy, S. *When Elephants Weep: The Emotional Lives of Animals.* Delacorte Press 1995.

Masson, J. *The Emperors Embrace: Reflections on Animal Families & Fatherhood.* Atria 1999.

Merfield, F.G. *Gorillas Were My Neighbours.* London: Longmans, Green & Co. 1956.

Merfield, F.G./Miller, H. *Gorilla Hunter.* New York: Farrar, Straus & Cudahy 1956.

Pepperberg, I. *The Alex Studies: Cognitive and Communicative Abilities of Grey Parrots.* Harvard University Press 1999.

Pocock, R. 1. *The Field,* Vol. 148, p. 707. London: October 21, 1926.

Pocock, R. l. *Proceedings of the Zoological Society,* pp. 543-91. London: 1932.

Reucassel, D. *The Ways of The Wild.* Johannesburg: Visual Teaching Aids 1987.

Roberts, A. *The mammals of South Africa.* Johannesburg: 'Mammals of South Africa' Book Fund 1951.

Schouteden, H. *Ann. Musée du Congo Belge,* Ser. II, Vol. III, pp. 169-332. Brussels: 1945.

Sclater, W. L. *The mammals of South Africa,* Vol. I. London: R.H. Porter 1900.

Shuker, K. P. N. *Mystery Cats of the World.* London: Robert Hale 1989.

Schaller, G.B*. *The Year of the Gorilla.* University Chicago Press 1964.

Tobias, P.V. Work of the gorilla research unit in Uganda: *Sth. African Journal Science,* 57 (11): 297-298, 1961.

Zahl, P. Face to face with gorillas in Central Africa: *National Geographic,* Vol. 117, No. 1. 1960.

Zimmerman, D. personal communication: letter to George Schaller*: detailing observation of black leopard stalking Mountain gorilla. Sept. 23, 1962.

❦   ❦

Bekoff, M. Editor: *The Smile Of A Dolphin.* London: Discovery Books 2000.

Bekoff, M. *Minding Animals: Awareness, emotion and heart.* Oxford University Press 2002.

de Waal, F. The Ape and the Sushi Master: Cultural reflections of a primatologist. Allen Lane 2001.

Gould, S.J. *The Hedgehog, The Fox and the Magister's Pox.* London: Jonathan Cape 2003.

Peterson, D./Ammann, K. *Eating Apes.* Berkeley: University of California Press 2003.

Sheldrake, R. Testing a Language-Using Parrot for Telepathy: *Journal of Scientific Exploration,* Vol. 17, No. 4, pp. 601-666, 2003.

Thurston, G. Nowhere to Hide: *BBC Wildlife* Vol. 19, No. 9, pp58-63, 2001.

Journey to the Gorillas

Uganda   Rwanda

The misty Virungas and alluring Bwindi Impenetrable Forest, Volcanoes National Park and Mgahinga National Park - last bastions of the Mountain Gorilla. In the most breathtaking locations commune with gorillas, climb a volcano, hike the magical Mountains of the Moon, cross pristine crater lakes by dug-out, go birding in true jungle, thrill at butterflies amassing in clouds. Volcanoes Safaris is the premier gorilla safari company of Uganda and Rwanda, offering style and elegance in remote parts in exclusive rest-camps and eco-friendly lodges, built with sensitivity in a culturally appropriate way, that are the best in the region.

Journey to the gorillas.

VOLCANOES SAFARIS

Uganda • Rwanda

www.volcanoessafaris.com

ILLUSTRATIONS

Adventure kit
for all seasons

Footloose in Africa, or wherever in the world you wander

Suppliers par excellence to the adventure traveller Fox's of Old Amersham
stock every leading brand in adventure clothing, footwear and
equipment - its outdoor footwear department is the largest in Britain - from
camping furniture and climbing gear, maps, medical kits and mosquito nets,
sleeping bags and tropic safari wear, to navigation aids and hydration
systems. Situated in the heart of England's picturesque Chilterns, Fox's is a
veritable Aladdin's Cave of outdoor adventure kit 'for all seasons', tailor-
made for the traveller to Africa…… or wherever in the world you wander.

London Road, Amersham England
www.foxsoutdoor.co.uk

FOX'S
ADVENTURE CLOTHING
AND EQUIPMENT

GLOSSARY

Afro-alpine zone
Limit of Africa's montane fauna, dominated by arborescent plants, tarns, lakes and frozen waterfalls.

Aardvark hole
A burrow dug in the side of a termite mound by an aardvark or antbear, a distinctive pig-like animal with elongated snout and powerful claws that feeds mainly on termites and ants.

Ant-heap
Bush vernacular for a mound created by flying "white ants" (termites) living in an organised colony. Termitariums may reach 3m in height; many can exceed this. Deserted ones can have trees up to 100 years old growing off them.

Boomslang
Slender snake favouring tree/shrub cover hence its name 'tree snake' from the Afrikaans *boom* for tree and *slang* for snake. Back-fanged and placid they were popular pets with boys in colonial Africa, until their venom was found to be among the most potent known, giving rise to brisk announcements in schools across 1950s Rhodesia and adjacent parts for those with a *boomslang* at school to "report to the Headmaster forthwith"!

Bongo
Forest relative of Eland inhabiting central Africa's rainforests, bushy thickets and bamboo jungle up to 4,000m. Both sexes bear horns with which they'll defend courageously. A shy browser unique, for its size, for being at home in dense cover, bongo aren't numerous, with numbers threatened by further destruction of forest habitat.

Bonobo
Aka 'pygmy chimps', bonobo are slender, but generally no smaller. A female-centric society, where the feeding routine involves little friction, females bond, fighting is rare, sex is used as an appeasing force, and mother-son bonds last a lifetime, sets bonobos apart from common chimps - findings that irresistibly lead to the notion that bonobos are better role models for human behaviour, and as such far more attractive candidates for ancestor!

Colobus
Thumbless arboreal monkeys of the sub-family *Colobinae,* where the thumb is vestigial or absent. With complex stomachs adapted for a vegetarian diet around 10 species divided into black and white, red and olive colobus occur in Africa's forested parts. Long, silky fur once made black and white colobus, some known as guerezas, so prized in Europe a century or so back that large numbers were slaughtered annually.

Dew claw
Claw terminating the fifth toe pad, and not reaching to the ground, on the forepaw of a felid. Corresponding to a human thumbnail, it is much relied upon in climbing, for holding prey, and can inflict deadly damage in an attack.

Disruptive camouflage
'Dismembering colouration' where stripes, blotches or rosettes disrupt the impression of a solid form to allow an animal to blend into its surrounds, as with giraffe, zebra, tiger, or leopard patterning, and most notably the infinitely versatile dual-camouflage of King Cheetah, supreme evolutionary exemplar of *punctuated equilibrium*.

Duiker
Small, territorial, primarily nocturnal browsing antelopes named from the Dutch for 'diving' into cover. Divided into Forest and Bush categories, with a colour range from red to blue-grey, the former has the majority species, both sexes bearing horns; the latter is one widespread species with many local races where females are often larger.

Fever tree
The lovely Yellow-barked Acacia, dubbed long ago the *Fever tree* due to being unfairly associated with malaria, maybe yellow fever too - where these water-loving trees thrived, went the logic, so did mosquitoes!

Flying squirrel
Attractive squirrel-like, big eyed, bushy-tailed mammals with a "gliding" flap of furred skin stretched from neck and wrist to the ankle and base of the tail with, on the underside of the latter, two rows of sharp-pointed scales to aid climbing. Numbering several species of a family extinct outside tropical Africa, the tiniest, the pretty miniature Pygmy or Zenker's flying squirrel, averages an HB length of just 7cm.

Forest buffalo
The little red buffalo or Dwarf buffalo from Central Africa's forests, with more modest horns than black Cape Buffalo, that sweep backwards and lack the great frontal bosses. Intermediate stages exist between the two types.

Genet
Lissom nocturnal carnivore tamed in ancient Egypt. A skilful tree climber, quite cat-like in appearance, it will even arch its back and hiss. Considered by some to be relatives of mongoose, a number of species, generally spotted with bushy banded tails, are recognised for Africa, but the classification of *Genetta* in Africa is still uncertain.

Giant forest hog
Largest of Africa's wild pigs, a metre at the shoulder, weighing up to 230kg or 500lbs, living in small families in dense thickets and open stands in Central Africa's forest belt. May mate for life.

Giant Groundsel
Bizarre cabbage-headed *Senecios* growing up to 9m tall, which with pillaresque Lobelias that shoot 2-3m from a leafy rosette base, are unique to Africa's high peaks, with species of each endemic to the different mountain areas.

Golden Monkey
Rare and attractive intraspecific variation of the Blue Monkey, or Diademed Guenon *Cercopithecus mitus.*

Guenons
Graceful quadrupedal monkeys of the family *Cercopithecidae* only occurring in Africa south of the Sahara, with prodigiously long tails that exceed their HB length, and a talent for using mimicry and a variety of gestures to communicate. Includes De Brazza, Blue monkey, and L'Hoest, the latter the only one with a semi-prehensile tail.

Hypericum trees

Literally giant versions of the humble St. John's Wort, a modest shrub in temperate zones, that grow as trees - with brilliant yellow, or orange, rose or tulip-like flowers - up to 15m tall in the high altitude forests of Africa's equatorial regions.

Kopje

Rocky hills or inselbergs - literally 'island mountains' - confined to the tropics. Formed of granite and covered in scrub, rocks and boulders, kopjes range from modest rocky piles, to great castle-like, crenellated hills of boulders balanced on top of each other, and towering hundreds of feet above flat bush country.

Mange

A debilitating, contagious skin disease in animals caused by any of several varieties of mites. Transmitted between animals by direct contact, most mange mites infest only one species. Fatal if untreated, the most severe are notoedric mange or feline scabies, and sarcoptic mange - true scabies - common in canids and humans.

Miombo

A vast mass of savanna woodland spreading across the plateaux of south Central Africa - one of the most immense, uniform tracts of bush country or *bundu* in Africa, with different designations according to area - extending 1,300-1,900kms south from the Congo River to below the Zambezi, and some 2,400kms coast to coast, riven by rifts and flood plains, and recently as the 1920s abounding in game.

Mountain gorilla

As distinguished from Eastern lowland gorilla (eastern Congo rainforests) and Western lowland gorilla (Cameroon, CAR, Congo, Gabon, Equatorial Guinea). Despite Lowland gorillas generally being considered more numerous, the lowland Western race is so fragmented by poaching for meat, sorcery and trade it's arguable just how less threatened. Just 600+/- Mountain gorillas are reckoned to be surviving in the Virungas and neighbouring reserves, with those outside Virunga being possibly an intermediate type.

Mountains of the Moon

Name owed to Claudius Ptolemaeus (2nd. cent. AD) based on travellers tales for the fabled snow-capped Rwenzoris, the range of equatorial mountains with its numerous individual peaks (highest 5,110m) that stretches 120kms down Africa's Western Rift Valley. Known to the ancient Mediterranean world from at least 450BC - earliest contacts possibly the Egyptians before 2000BC - Ptolemy in his *Guide to Geography* has the 'Lunae Montes' as the ultimate source of the Nile. See Parke below.

Muhavura

Mountain in the Virungas, a chain of eight volcanoes straddling Uganda, Rwanda and Congo in three groups. It is the most easterly of the eastern group, and with Gahinga, Sabinyo and three neighbouring volcanoes, home to the true Mountain gorilla. Astride Uganda and Rwanda *Muhavura* has long been a beacon, visible from afar. Towering up 4,130m it is only outstripped by Karisimbi and Mikeno of the central group (each over 4,400m.). Volcanic activity persists to this day in the most westerly of the volcanoes, Nyamulagira and Nyiragongo.

Pangolin

A name aptly derived from the Malay *peng-goling* for 'roller', pangolins are scaly anteaters in an order of their own, in a single family and a single genus of some seven species, four of which reside in Africa, two arboreal and two terrestrial.

Parke

The brave and extraordinary Surgeon Major Thomas Heazle Parke, first modern European to sight the Mountains of the Moon (though Stanley later usurped this claim for himself), and first Irishman to cross Africa from coast to coast (1889). A splendid life size bronze statue of Parke stands out front the Natural History Museum Dublin.

Podo tree

The magnificent yellow wood tree of the genus *Podocarpus*. A characteristic highland tree of East Africa, growing in parts up to 100 ft. tall, its spreading crown can shed rain so efficiently outward the tree makes an ideal dry shelter; indeed, Podo bases being so dry may account for them never appearing to be struck by lightning.

Potto

Endearing, bear-like primates found only in woodlands and forests. Of the two species in Africa, each in a genera of their own, the more widely spread Bosman's potto - larger and more attractive of the two - on finding itself in enemy territory near its claimant, will 'play possum' by keeping still to elude detection.

Pugmark

The footprint of an animal, after the Hindi for foot; notably that of a wild mammal.

Raptor

Deriving from the Latin "to seize and carry off". Generally any bird of prey, though sometimes restricted to diurnal birds of prey: hawks, eagles, vultures, buzzards etc. In the broader sense it's simply synonymous with the designation "bird of prey" and thereby embraces the nocturnal birds of prey, the owls.

Spoor

A trail of pugmarks or tracks, droppings, scents, sounds and other traces of an animal's passage. Interpreted as "ground" spoor by way of pugs on the ground, together with "aerial" spoor in sign left on or above ground, *viz* droppings; sticks, stones or vegetation disturbed; broken spiderwebs, traces of fur, smells etc.

Stinkwood

The Red Stinkwood tree, *Pygeum Africanum* - a tall forest tree with small white flowers which gives out a smell like cyanide when the bark is scored.

Tree heather

Actual trees of flowering heather, small bushes elsewhere, that from around 1,800m up the slopes of the mountains of the equatorial regions of Africa grow in forest belts of trees up to as much as 16m and more in height, on boles the size of pines.

228

Tree hyrax

Mainly arboreal member of the hyrax/dassie family: an attractive mammal resembling a marmot, the size of a large rabbit and mostly adapted to rocky habitats, hence the common name "rock rabbit". While there's little to distinguish one from another in the field, the *Tree hyrax* is recognisable by a preference for hollow trees or dense foliage high up, and for eerie wails uttered after dusk that rise to a piercing scream.

Tsetse fly

A name derived from the Tswana language, said to suggest the buzzing of the fly, and confined to Africa. More than half the approx. 21 species of tsetse transmit *sleeping sickness* to humans, and *nagana* to domestic stock. Feeding on blood, there's currently no really effective controls beyond environmental ones.

Vibrissae

The bristly hairs on an animal's face, notably the whiskers of a cat. Heaviest around the upper lips, with some on each cheek, chin and above the eyes, they're important tactile organs that supply information about surroundings. As the slightest movement stimulates nerve endings, vibrissae may detect deflected air currents, and with special muscles to move them, can even be put on alert.

Viscera

The soft contents of the principal cavities of the body, *viz* the internal organs: especially heart, liver, kidneys, together with the intestines.

Vlei

Common *Afrikaans* expression in general usage throughout southern Africa for a watery meadow or marshy depression where water collects in the *wet* season; aka *dambo* in central and East Africa for a small grassy floodplain; also other native names according to the locale.